Stories from the Canadian North

Stories from the Canadian North

Edited by
Muriel Whitaker

Illustrated by
Vlasta van Kampen

Hurtig Publishers
Edmonton

For Mary Ellen and Lloyd

Hurtig Publishers Ltd.
10560 - 105 Street
Edmonton, Alberta
T5H 2W7

Canadian Cataloguing in Publication Data

Main entry under title:
Stories from the Canadian north

ISBN 0-88830-188-X

1. Short stories, Canadian (English).*
2. Canada, Northern — Fiction.   I. Whitaker,
Muriel A., 1923-   II. van Kampen, Vlasta.
PS8323.N6S8   C813'.0108'32719   C80-091013-3
PR9197.3.S8

Printed and bound in Canada

Contents

Acknowledgements

The editor wishes to thank the following for permission to include in this anthology previously copyrighted material:

"The Shaman" from *The White Dawn* by James Houston, reprinted by permission of Academic Press Canada.

"The Blind Boy and the Loon" from *Tales from the Igloo* by Maurice Metayer, reprinted by permission of Hurtig Publishers.

"Left Behind" from *Land of the Good Shadows* by Heluiz Chandler Washburne and Anauta (John Day Co.). Copyright 1940, renewed 1968 by Heluiz Chandler Washburne. Reprinted by permission of Harper & Row, Publishers, Inc.

"Mothers of the North" from *More Kindred of the Wild* by Charles G. D. Roberts, reprinted by permission of Ward Lock Ltd.

"The Furs" from *Agaguk* by Yves Thériault. Translated by Miriam Chapin. Copyright © The Ryerson Press, 1963. Reprinted by permission of McGraw-Hill Ryerson Limited.

"Walk Well, My Brother" from *The Snow Walker* by Farley Mowat, reprinted by permission of The Canadian Publishers, McClelland and Stewart Limited, Toronto.

No Canadian is more highly regarded among the Eskimos of the eastern Arctic than James Houston (1921-   ). Born in Ontario and trained as an artist, Houston made his first trip to the Arctic in 1948 and it was there that he became acquainted with traditional Inuit art – carvings in bone, stone, and ivory. In 1951 he was appointed the first civil administrator of West Baffin Island. After serving in that position for nine years, he continued to live on the island for several years and during this time he introduced the Japanese art of stone-block printing to the Eskimos with such success that Cape Dorset prints are now collectors' items all over the world. In addition to making prints, the Eskimos were encouraged to produce sculptures and garments that were sold through the West Baffin Eskimo Co-operative. In tribute to Houston's initiative, the well-known artist Pitseolak has said that he was "the first man to help Eskimos. Ever since he came the Eskimo people have been able to find work. Here in Cape Dorset they call him 'The Man'."

Since leaving the Arctic, Houston has been a sculptor; a designer and an executive of Steuben Glass in New York; a member of the Canadian Arts Council; and the author and illustrator of a number of books, including *Wolf Run; a Caribou Eskimo Tale* (1971), *Songs of the Dream People* (1972), *Kiviok's Magic Journey* (1973), *Ghost Fox* (1977), and *River Runners* (1979).

"The Shaman" is taken from *The White Dawn* (1971), an "Eskimo Saga" about the lives and violent deaths of three American whalers who were cast into the Stone Age life of an Eskimo community on West Baffin Island after becoming separated from their ship while harpooning a whale. The story is based on an event recorded in the log of the sailing bark *Escoheag* on May 16, 1896, and perpetuated in the memories of the Eskimos.

The shaman was probably the most important individual in Eskimo society for he was the mediator between the people and the supernatural powers that controlled their lives. The most powerful and dangerous of the spirits was the sea-goddess Nuliayuk since she could withhold from the people the seals, whales, polar bears, and walruses that were said to have been created from her severed fingers. It was believed that failure to observe the elaborate system of taboos would so anger the goddess that she would punish the people with sickness and starvation. The shaman would communicate with her by holding public seances.

Knud Rasmussen, a Danish ethnologist whose studies are an important source of information about Eskimo mythology, repeatedly asked the reasons for the rituals and taboos. An Iglulik leader gave him this answer:

We fear the weather spirit of earth that we
     must fight
against to wrest our food from land and
     sea. We fear Sila.
We fear death and hunger in the cold snow
     huts.
We fear Takanakapsâluk, the great
     woman down at the bottom
of the sea...
Therefore it is that our fathers have
     inherited from their
fathers all the old rules of life which are
     based on the
experience and wisdom of generations.

This atmosphere is well evoked by the narrator of *The White Dawn,* the crippled son of the headman, Sarkak.

The Shaman

James Houston

All of our meat was gone, and the dogs roamed through the camp like starved wolves, afraid of humans, yet cunning in their thievery, for they would gobble up a dropped mitt or gnaw the sealskin lashings off a sled. Sarkak paced among the snowhouses like a bear, staring at the bleary moon, trying to gauge the weather. That night he tossed on the bed without sleeping, and perhaps seeing some vision in the shadows, he called out, commanding Kangiak and Yaw to hitch a team and travel back to the land, to go to the shaman's camp. He told them to bring the shaman to our camp as quickly as they could, for something was wrong. It was strange that the seals had gone. Someone must have broken a taboo, and for this we might die. If we returned to the land starving and without meat, we would never again feel the warmth of summer.

We gave up hunting and waited for the shaman, fearing now that anything we did might make the situation worse. Our women stood in the entrance porches, jogging to keep warm and to soothe their hungry babies. They stared to the northeast, eager to have a glimpse of the returning sled, and when it finally reappeared, we were all relieved to see that the shaman and his dirty boy were on it with Kangiak and Yaw.

The shaman was tired, he said, and marched straight into Sarkak's house before he was asked, lay down in the center of the bed and went to sleep. Just before arriving at our nearly starving camp, he had slyly eaten some meat, and it was not until the twilight of noon that he arose on the following day.

Many gathered in Sarkak's big igloo, as many as could find room to stand. Even the side house, the empty meat porch and the entrance tunnel were jammed with women and children who could not see but hoped to hear some of what was said. I stood in a place where I could watch both the shaman and Sarkak. The three foreigners placed themselves boldly before this magical man, who sat on the snow platform. They eyed him intently, and Pilee had a half smile on his face, not at all friendly, but mean and sneering.

I could see that the shaman pretended to look at others, but he was always aware of the *kalunait*. He had never spoken to us about these three, and it had been as though he did not recognize their existence. But now he spoke out. He pursed his lips and spoke quickly, using words strung together in a way that was hard to understand. I could tell that Kakuktak was listening carefully, but I think he understood none of it.

"Have you been visited by foreigners?" asked the shaman, as if he did not know.

There was a pause. Then everyone answered, "Yes."

"Perhaps they have brought with them some kind of evil that drives away the sea beasts," said the shaman.

"Yes...perhaps," answered all the people.

"Have these foreigners been fortunate in hunting?"

"No," answered the people.

One of the hunters spoke up. "Only the big one, who has had three walrus and one seal, and the yellow-headed one, who has brought us many birds."

"Birds! Only birds," sneered the shaman. "That is no wonder with those great snowmen standing in this camp."

He tied a band of skin around his forehead, grabbed up a snow knife, and tossing another to the dirty boy, ran out of the house. We hurried out after them, not wishing to miss anything, but, as always, because of my legs, I was the last to struggle outside, just in time to see the first snow figure come crashing down. Then over the top of Poota's snowhouse I saw the second figure, facing north, lean and break into pieces as it fell. The figure facing west toppled next, and I saw the shaman run up, gasping for breath, and with his snow knife slash down the last figure. He tramped and kicked apart its crumbled remains, and when that was done, he turned away in disgust and led us back down into the big snowhouse, all except the children and some of the women who were afraid.

No one spoke, and every eye turned toward the three *kalunait*. Some perhaps started thinking of them in a new way.

"These three strangers, these dog children," said the shaman, "they have returned to this land. Who can say if that is good? We can try only to listen and to understand the signs.

"I will tell you of the dog children again, for some of you may have forgotten and some young people may not have heard the story. A long time ago there was a seal hunter who had a daughter, and she thought that the young man whom her father had chosen for her was not good enough. So her father grew angry and said to her, 'For a husband you should have my dog.'

"That night a handsome stranger entered their igloo. No one had ever seen him before. They noticed that he wore a beautiful close-fitting parka, and he had a sinew necklace around his neck. On each side of his chest hung large canine teeth. The stranger was welcomed into their bed, and he coupled with the hunter's daughter in a strange fashion. When they awoke in the morning, he was gone.

"The father worried about the visitor for five whole moons, and then he was certain that the stranger must have been his dog disguised as a man. He was sure that his daughter was with child, and being ashamed of this inhuman affair, he made the girl lie on the deck of his kayak. He paddled her out to a small island and left her there. But the girl did not die, for the dog man reappeared, and holding meat in his teeth, each day he swam over to the island and fed her. One day the hunter saw the dog man doing this and struck him over the head with the sharp edge of his paddle and drowned him.

"When the girl was weak with hunger, she brought forth six children. Three were *innuit*, true people like ourselves, and the other three were half dog and half human. She was ashamed of these dog children and knew that they would all starve. So she took a sealskin and fashioned a boot sole, curled like a boat. In it she placed the three dog children and shoved them off, southward toward the open sea. As they floated away, she called after them, '*Sarutiktapsinik sanavagumarkpusi.* You shall be skillful at making weapons.'

"Now look before you at these three, the offspring of those dog children, bastards, returned to us now with their sharp weapons, their iron knives."

I saw many people in our camp draw back in shock and horror. Our people had only vaguely thought of these three as dog children, but they had forgotten its real meaning, and now the ghostly impact of the inhuman father came to them. It would cause the women to fear the foreigners and the children to run from them.

"*Ayii,*" said the people, full of uneasiness and suspicion. "We understand you."

The shaman held up his hands and said, "Someone is trying to speak to me. Listen. Listen."

We all listened, and the shaman began to cough. His coughing continued until he went into a great fit of hacking and strangling. When he straightened up, his face was flushed and red, and he growled like a dog. He whined and said words we could not understand.

The shadows of so many people standing in the snowhouse made the light faint, but I, myself, clearly saw what happened next, and Sarkak saw it and the three strangers saw it. The shaman swayed back as though he had been struck a powerful blow on the head, and he let out a horrible inhuman howl. As he opened his mouth, I could see great curved white dog teeth on either side of his jaws. He began snapping his teeth, and foam appeared at the sides of his mouth. It was flecked with blood. He was like a man gone mad.

Tugak reached out and held him by the arms, and the dirty boy leaped forward and also grabbed the shaman. They all three struggled violently. Everyone drew back in fear and horror. Had we not seen the mysterious dog man appearing before us, half hidden in the fat body of the shaman? At last the violent struggling ceased, and the shaman lay in their arms, pale and trembling, his face and hair streaming with sweat.

"Open your mouth. Show us your teeth," many called to him.

The dirty boy took him roughly by the chin and pulled back his lips, but the great dog teeth had disappeared. A babble of frightened whispers raced around the snowhouse, and those inside called out to the people in the passage, telling them of the magic teeth and of how they had suddenly appeared and just as quickly disappeared.

The shaman was given water, and slowly he revived. He talked of seals, carefully referring to them only as *puyee*, sea beasts, so that those hidden listeners beneath the house would not fully understand his plans. Shamans have a whole language of their own, with different words for every animal and fish and bird. I could tell that our shaman had been teaching the dirty boy this language, and sometimes his helper understood, and sometimes he did not. The shaman now raised himself up on the bed, and he said a word many times, but we could all see that the dirty boy did not understand. The shaman grew angry, struck him across the side of the head and made him get out of the snowhouse and be by himself in the cold and darkness.

When the boy came back, Sarkak and the shaman were talking, and everyone else was listening. So excited was I that this time seemed endless.

The shaman suddenly coughed again and then howled like a dog and curled his lips into a snarl. His eyes narrowed, and his shoulders hunched like a dog ready to fight, but in an instant the expression was gone. Then it came to him again and left him once more. The shaman gasped like a running man and begged for a harpoon. We believed that he would use it to fight off the dreadful dog spirit that tore at his anus, trying to enter his body.

Sarkak called for this weapon, and in a moment one was handed to him, a short broad walrus harpoon with a strong driftwood shaft and a long ivory shank holding a sharpened blade in place.

When the shaman had the spear, he placed its butt on the floor of the snowhouse, and kneeling on the sleeping platform, he held the harpoon shaft with the point directed at his chest. Fascinated, horrified, our people drew back, crushing each other against the snow walls, yet frantically anxious to see everything that might occur.

The heavy shaman started swaying his soft womanlike body from side to side, rolling on his knees, singing in a high unreal voice. We could understand only some of the words:

> Ayii, ayii,
> Come. Come to me again,
> Father of these dog children.
> You with the big teeth,
> Enter into me. Enter into me.

Then he stopped singing and started to tremble. A howl escaped from his lips, and snarling, he howled again and lunged forward, straight onto the upturned point of the harpoon. He screamed as it pierced his soft belly and forced its way through him. He flung back his head and stared at all of us with terrible bulging, dying eyes. Blood gushed out of his mouth and ran down his parka and splashed over the snow floor. He fell from the bench and lashed and twisted in his death throes, clutching madly at the shaft of the harpoon.

Women and children screamed, and even the men in the passageway rushed out in fear. Roaring, he followed them into the blackness. He ran once around the snowhouse and then darted back into the passageway. We gasped in disbelief to see that he was once again a whole man.

He leered and smiled at us, holding his arms outstretched. He flung down the red harpoon and wiped the blood away from his face carelessly with his sleeve. We could see the gaping holes in the front and back of his parka where the sharp head of the harpoon had entered and emerged from his body, for he turned for us to see them. Then slowly he raised his parka and exposed his great round belly. It was smooth and unmarked, showing neither wound nor blood.

There was absolute silence in the room.

The shaman said in a wild strong voice, "The dog man is dead." He stood in triumph, staring scornfully at the three foreigners, these true descendants of the dog man.

I thought of them again and looked into their faces as they examined the shaman with looks of horror, for they, like ourselves, had been standing almost beside him and had watched him fall heavily onto the killing point of the harpoon. How could he now stand here before us unharmed?

Pilee and the big Portagee turned and left the snowhouse, but Kakuktak remained, sitting motionless beside Neevee. This should have been a time to eat, to feed our guest and to think of all that had happened. The fact that we had no food and the lamp burned with short flames for want of seal oil reminded us of all our troubles. No one moved or said a word.

The shaman called for a sleeping skin and went into the small side room that had been built for guests and the foreigners. He tied one end of this cover to a drying rack that had been driven into the snow wall, and he handed the other end to the dirty boy to hold. Then he asked for the small drum that he had brought with him. The light of both lamps was extinguished, and those who most feared darkness left the house. The old widow started singing madly, and they asked Nuna to take her mother to another igloo.

The shaman sat for a very long time behind the sealskin cover. All I could hear was his heavy breathing and an occasional tap he gave his drum. Suddenly he gasped and began talking in a deep heavy voice, and then he answered in a high voice, calling out the words, "Moon. Moon. Moon." The drumbeats became sharp and rapid, and the stiff sealskin trembled as though it were held in a high wind. The voice behind the hanging skin grew weaker and seemed to go away from us, calling, calling as it flew farther away, until there was a long silence, and I believed that the fat shaman had flown from the house. Then a sound seemed to come to us again, high in the air, and it rushed down to us, the voice growing louder and louder. It was not the sound of the shaman any more, but a deep booming voice. It came into the igloo and sat behind the trembling blanket.

On that night I heard for the first time the throbbing voice of the moon spirit. Like the others, I held my hand before my eyes, so afraid was I that I would go blind if I saw this monstrous glowing *tornraksoak* with his great dog team. It was said that he sometimes came among our people like a night shadow and secretly lay with our women. Indeed, sometimes I feared that he might have been my father. I trembled to think that he was so close to me.

The frightened women started singing, *"Amayii, amayii,"* trying to find courage in their endless choruses. But the bitter body smell of fear filled the house, and the older women placed their hands between their legs to protect themselves from the penetrations of the moon spirit.

Then I heard the moon spirit strike the drum edge twice and fly away from us, his voice growing weaker and weaker as he rose again into the night sky. For some time there was silence in the snowhouse, and you could hear the sound of people breathing. Then with a slow tapping the drumming began again, and in this way we knew that the shaman had returned to us. The dirty boy called for the lamp and took down the sealskin cover, and again we saw the shaman. He lay face down, pale and trembling, and it seemed to me that his body had been used by Takkuk, the moon spirit.

As the shaman was reviving, he called for bone chisels and directed that a hole be cut down through the ice floor. Sowniapik and Tungilik began this with great vigor, then changed with others, their faces glistening with sweat. Portagee and Kakuktak each took a turn, laughing and chopping down with all their strength. The young women, hot with excitement because they had felt the moon spirit so near them, chanted chorus after chorus, faster and faster, in time with the pounding chisels and the flying chips of ice. Okalikjuak gave a shout as his point broke through and the dark waters of the sea flooded the hole.

The shaman raised his hand and approached the hole cautiously, peering down into the water. Then he called out strange words and shouted, "Nuliayuk. Nuliayuk." Without having to ask, Sarkak waved, and the people crouched in the entrance passage passed in a new sealskin line, tightly coiled and strong, about the thickness of my smallest finger.

The shaman listened and told the dirty boy to tie a running knot in the line, but when he failed at this, the shaman flew into a rage and struck him again across the side of the head. To hit someone in anger in the presence of others is never done by our people, and everyone drew back in shock. The

boy held his hands over his head, and the shaman pushed him violently into the entrance passage. He stumbled alone out into the blackness.

The shaman bent over the hole and became so stiff that he appeared frozen and alone under that dome crowded with people. In the end of the line he had himself made a running knot, and now with great care he lowered the loop down through the hole in the ice.

Of course, everyone knows of the great female spirit Nuliayuk, who lives in a house beneath the sea. Savage sea wolves guard the entrance to her house, and it is surrounded by long-clawed bears and bellowing walrus. Inside the house she sits and hoards the seals that swim in the immenseness of her lamp. Near the entrance passage sits her husband, Unga, a dwarf who still has feelings for the listeners at the breathing places, as he calls us, the true people who dwell above the ice of the sea.

Slowly the shaman lowered the long line until it was extended to its full length beneath the ice, and gently he called down into the hole, using kindly words, magical words. Suddenly I saw the line jerk violently downward, smashing the shaman's bare hands against the side of the hole in the ice floor. He lunged back, but the line was snapped downward again, and he braced himself against it. We could see it quivering like a bowstring.

"Help me! Help me!" he called.

But many were afraid to touch that line that stretched between ourselves and the awesome world beneath the sea.

Then Pilee stepped forward, with his hat on the side of his head and a smile on his face. He took the line. The shaman released his grip and Pilee was dragged to the floor and slipped and fell. Portagee and Kakuktak leaped forward and grabbed the line, and together, with tremendous effort, they drew the great weight upward, slowly, hand over hand. When the end was almost at the level of the ice, it jerked downward again, surprising them. The big Portagee let go, drawing back in horror. Kakuktak's face was pale and drawn. They had both felt the force of this unseen thing beneath the ice.

Sarkak called out, and his sons took the line and other hunters joined, including me. All together we hauled the trembling, jerking line upward.

Women and children screamed with fear.

Then the shaman shouted, "Release the seals. Release the seals," and suddenly the weight on the line was released, and the men fell backward onto the people who crouched against the wall.

I looked at Kakuktak, Pilee and Portagee. I could see that the three foreigners were nervous and excited, for they had not known what to make of the shaman's performance. They were still with Sarkak, they were a part of his household, and yet they were becoming a part of all of us, and we seemed to be a part of them. I wished that they had not seen the shaman perform his magic. I knew that they did not understand him. Because he was dirty and sly, they thought he should be deceitful also. But this was not so. His magic was very ancient, and it had come down to him from powerful shamans who, people knew, could fly in the air and leap into the dark caves beneath the earth. I have heard that some useless shamans dwelling west of us perform tricks such as carving bearlike teeth out of bone and slipping these into their mouths to frighten people. We also know the old trick of filling a short piece of seal intestine with blood. When tied at both ends and hidden in the mouth, it will break when bitten and cause a most convincing bleeding. But these three strangers could not know all this, and we had no words to tell them. They did not wish to believe what they had seen, and yet they had all three seen it, as we had, and it would haunt them forever.

It was hot in the snowhouse and full of nervousness. A fog had formed from our excited breathing and hung near the white domed ceiling that glistened with sweat. To cool my spinning head, I hobbled out into the darkness, where I happened to see the dirty boy running behind a snowhouse. He flung a coil of cut sealskin line and a knife up onto the igloo's dome so that they were hidden from my view, and this act of his made me suspicious. I followed his footsteps through the new salt rime on the snow and found the place where he had tramped around. Suddenly my foot slipped down through a newly made hole he had just covered, which had not yet frozen over. It was a small hole that he had chopped down into the sea. I was puzzled, for I could not at first imagine why he had made this hole and why he had then so carefully hidden it with snow. Then I thought that it might be part of a trick. I wondered whether the shaman had sent the line beneath the ice between two holes, as our fishermen do when they set our winter nets. If that were so, the dirty boy could have jerked the line to make us feel the hidden strength of the underwater spirit.

I put this stupid thought out of my mind and never mentioned it to a living person, until now.

Maurice Metayer (1914-1974) was born in St. Malo, France, and served for thirty-five years as an Oblate missionary to the Eskimos of the western Arctic. When he was dying of cancer, he wrote to his bishop: "My hands are still empty. I didn't accomplish anything that I set out to do. I have never produced anything but desires which have not been fulfilled." In fact, he accomplished a good deal. In addition to performing parochial duties at Cambridge Bay and other Arctic missions, his knowledge of the Eskimo language and his interest in Eskimo tradition led him to write a number of books, including *I, Nuligak,* the reminiscences of an Eskimo born in the Mackenzie Delta in 1895; *Eskimo Tradition of Coppermine Unipkat; Angadjustitka,* an Eskimo prayer book; and *Cantiques Esquimaux,* a hymn book. "The Blind Boy and the Loon" is taken from Father Metayer's collection of Copper Eskimo folk tales, *Tales from the Igloo* (1972).

In the book's preface Father Metayer describes the atmosphere in which the stories would have been told:

> Most often it was at night in the igloo, during the long winter evenings, that the old storytellers passed on legends of the past to the younger people. With a few taps of a stick one of the women extinguished the greater part of the wick of the stone lamp. A few flames still danced but gave little illumination. In this uncertain light the dome and the walls of the igloo became vague forms, dissolving the confines of the igloo as if the darkness of the night had entered....

No one was asleep in the igloo but each was on the verge of dreams. The voice of the storyteller rekindled the flames of the past while the present disappeared. It was the age of the ancestors that became reality and one relived the lives of heroes and performed heroic feats.

In order to understand fully the ending of "The Blind Boy and the Loon", one must realize that the Eskimo hero was predominantly an avenger. Just as the spirits of weather, thunder, lightning, and the sea took vengeance on those who mistreated them, so too was the mortal hero expected to have the will and the power to exact retribution for evil. Knud Rasmussen noted that in every Eskimo community he visited the men who had murdered others were not regarded as criminals but as the most worthy men in the tribe.

The Blind Boy and the Loon
Maurice Metayer

A woman lived with her son and daughter in a faraway land. The son, although young in years, was already a skillful hunter and the four storage platforms built around the igloo were always filled with meat. His success at hunting was so great that the family never wanted for anything.

The young hunter's sister loved him dearly but his mother gradually grew tired of his hunting activities. Each time her son returned home with some game she would have to work hard at cleaning and skinning the animals and in preparing the meat for storage. As time went on the woman wished more and more to be able to rest but as long as her son continued to hunt this was not possible. Eventually her weariness turned to hatred.

One day, while her son was sleeping, the woman took a piece of dirty blubber and rubbed it on his eyes, wishing as she did so that he would become blind. When the young man awoke his eyesight was gone. Try as he might he could see nothing but a dim whiteness.

From that day on increasing misery became the lot of the family. The son could do nothing but sit on his bed. His mother tried to provide food for the family by trapping foxes and hunting ptarmigan and ground squirrels. Yet when food was available the woman refused to give her son anything to eat or drink but the worst parts of the meat and some foul drinking water brought from the lake. Throughout the spring and summer the three people lived in this manner.

One day shortly after the arrival of winter, the young hunter heard steps on the snow. It was a polar bear trying to get into the igloo through the thin ice-window. Asking for his bow, he told his mother to aim the arrow while he pulled back the string. When all was in readiness the son let fly the arrow. Hearing the sound of the arrow as it thudded into the flesh of the bear, the son was confident that the kill had been made.

"I got him!" he cried.

"No," retorted his mother, "you merely struck an old piece of hide."

Shortly thereafter the smell of bear meat boiling in the cooking pot filled the igloo. The son said nothing but kept wondering why his mother had lied to him.

When the meat was cooked the woman fed her daughter and herself. To her son, she gave some old fox meat. It was only when she had left the igloo to get water from the lake that the young hunter was brought some bear meat by his sister.

Four long years went by while the son remained blind. Then one night, as the fluttering of wings and the cries of the birds announced the coming of spring, the son heard the call of the red-throated loon. As had been his habit during his blindness he began to crawl on his hands and knees to the lake where he knew the loon would be found.

When he arrived at the water's edge the bird came close to him and said, "Your mother made you blind by rubbing dirt into your eyes while you slept. If you wish, I can wash your eyes for you. Lie flat on my back and hold me by my neck. I shall carry you."

The son doubted that such a small bird would be able to perform such a feat, but the loon reassured him.

"Don't think those thoughts. Climb onto my back. I am going to dive with you into deep water. When you begin to lose your breath shake your body to signal me."

The young man did as he was told and down into the lake dove the loon with the hunter on his back. As they descended into the water the son could feel the body of the loon growing larger and larger and between his hands the neck seemed to be swelling. When he could hold his breath no longer he shook his body as he had been instructed and the loon brought him up to the surface.

"What can you see?" the loon asked.

"I can see nothing but a great light," replied the son.

"I shall take you down into the water once more," said the loon. "When you begin to choke, shake your body a little."

This time the dive lasted a long time but when they finally surfaced the young man could see clearly. He could distinguish the smallest rocks on the mountains far away. He described what he could see to the loon.

"My blindness is gone! My sight is sharper than before!"

"Your eyesight is too sharp for your own good," the loon told him. "Come down with me once more and your sight will be restored as it was before your blindness."

And it was so. When the young man came out of the water for the last time his eyesight was as it had been. Now the hunter could see the loon clearly and he realized that the bird was as large as a kayak.

When they had reached the lake shore the son asked the loon what he could give to him in return for his kindness.

The loon replied, "I do not want anything for myself other than a few fishes. Put some in the lake for me once in a while. This is the only food that I look for."

The son agreed and proceeded to return to his home. He was painfully surprised to see the wretched conditions in which he had been forced to live while he was blind. The skins he had used to sleep in were filthy with dirt and bugs. His drinking water and food were crawling with lice. Nevertheless he sat down in the corner and waited for his mother to awaken.

When his mother awoke the young hunter asked for food and drink. "I am hungry and thirsty. First bring me something to drink."

His mother did as she was told but the water she brought was so dirty that her son handed the cup back to her saying, "I will not touch such filth!"

"So you can see, my son," said the woman. She went then to fetch some clean food and water.

In time the young hunter was his old self again and was able to resume his successful hunting trips as before. A year went by during which time the storage platforms were once more filled with an abundance of game.

The following spring the hunter made ready to go whale hunting. He put a new skin cover on his whale boat, made lines, harpoons and spears. When the sea was free of ice he launched his boat and took his mother with him in search of whales.

"Mind the helm," he told her. "I shall look after the harpooning."

Here and there they saw a few whales blowing but the young hunter was waiting until they found a big one close to their boat. Eventually he called out to his mother who, not knowing what her son was about to do, came to assist him. He threw his harpoon, making certain that its head had caught in the flesh of the whale and then quickly tied the other end of the line to his mother's wrist and threw her overboard.

Caught as she was the woman was dragged through the water, bobbing up and down in the waves. She cried out and reproached her son saying, "When you were young I gave you my breast to suckle. I fed you and kept you clean. And now you do this to me!"

Finally she disappeared from sight. For years to come hunters claimed that they saw her in the waves and heard her song of despair as it was carried far and wide by the winds.

Jack London (1876-1916) was born in San Francisco. A rolling stone, he spent his youth loafing in saloons on the Oakland waterfront, working in a cannery, riding freights, reading socialist literature, and developing a gift as a storyteller. In the summer of 1897, he joined the rush to the Klondike, packing a thousand pounds of supplies (a hundred pounds at a time) over the notorious Chillcoot Pass, and then building boats to navigate Lake Linderman and the Yukon River. During the winter he spent in a log cabin seventy-two miles from Dawson City, London listened to the stories of trappers, Indians, "Yellow Legs", seasoned sourdoughs, and hopeful treasure hunters. These tales and his own experiences were to provide rich source material for his short stories on the Yukon. By spring he was so sick with scurvy that he had to abandon the Klondike without ever staking a claim, but according to his biographer, Irving Stone, he "was to make more money out of the gold rush than any sourdough who staked a claim on Bonanza Creek".

In "The Sickness of Lone Chief" the central character looks back nostalgically to the good days before the steamboat came. London, however, shared the Victorian belief that native peoples, "lesser breeds without the law", were in need of the civilization that white men would bring in the form of hospitals, schools, and courts. Perhaps that is why he chose to depict the Indians before their contact with white men as superstitious, violent, and vengeful though he undoubtedly admired their ability to endure in a harsh environment. London's Yukon stories include *God of Their Fathers: Tales of the Klondike and the Yukon* (1902), *Children of the Forest* (1902), *The Call of the Wild* (1903), and *White Fang* (1906).

The Sickness of Lone Chief
Jack London

This is a tale that was told to me by two old men. We sat in the smoke of a mosquito-smudge, in the cool of the day, which was midnight; and ever and anon, throughout the telling, we smote lustily and with purpose at such of the winged pests as braved the smoke for a snack at our hides. To the right, beneath us, twenty feet down the crumbling bank, the Yukon gurgled lazily. To the left, on the rose-leaf rim of the low-lying hills, smouldered the sleepy sun, which saw no sleep that night nor was destined to see sleep for many nights to come.

The old men who sat with me and valorously slew mosquitoes were Lone Chief and Mutsak, erstwhile comrades in arms, and now withered repositories of tradition and ancient happening. They were the last of their generation and without honour among the younger set which had grown up on the farthest fringe of a mining civilisation. Who cared for tradition in these days, when spirits could be evoked from black bottles, and black bottles could be evoked from the complaisant white men for a few hours' sweat or a mangy fur? Of what potency the fearful rites and masked mysteries of shamanism, when daily that living wonder the steamboat coughed and spluttered up and down the Yukon, in defiance of all law, a veritable fire-breathing monster? And of what value was hereditary prestige, when he who now chopped the most wood, or best conned a stern-wheeler through the island mazes, attained the chiefest consideration of his fellows?

Of a truth, having lived too long, they had fallen on evil days, these two old men, Lone Chief and Mutsak, and in the new order they were without honour or place. So they waited drearily for death, and the while their hearts warmed to the strange white man who shared with them the torments of the mosquito-smudge and lent ready ear to their tales of old time before the steamboat came.

"So a girl was chosen for me," Lone Chief was saying. His voice, shrill and piping, ever and again dropped plummet-like into a hoarse and rattling bass, and, just as one became accustomed to it, soaring upward into the thin treble – alternate cricket chirpings and bullfrog croakings, as it were.

"So a girl was chosen for me," he was saying. "For my father, who was Kask-ta-ka, the Otter, was angered because I looked not with a needy eye upon women. He was an old man, and chief of his tribe. I was the last of his sons to be alive, and through me, only, could he look to see his blood go down among those to come after and as yet unborn. But know, O White Man, that I was very sick; and when neither the hunting nor the fishing delighted me, and by meat my belly was not made warm, how should I look with favour upon women? or prepare for the feast of marriage? or look forward to the prattle and troubles of little children?"

"Ay," Mutsak interrupted. "For had not Lone Chief fought in the arms of a great bear till his head was cracked and blood ran from out his ears?"

Lone Chief nodded vigorously. "Mutsak speaks true. In the time that followed, my head was well, and it was not well. For though the flesh healed and the sore went away, yet was I sick inside. When I walked, my legs shook under me, and when I looked at the light, my eyes became filled with tears. And when I opened my eyes, the world outside went around and around, and when I closed my eyes, my head inside went around and around, and all the things I had ever seen went around and around inside my head. And above my eyes there was a great pain, as though something heavy rested always upon them, or like a band that is drawn tight and gives much hurt. And speech was slow to me, and I waited long for each right word to come to my tongue. And when I waited not long, all manner of words crowded in, and my tongue spoke foolishness. I was very sick, and when my father, the Otter, brought the girl Kasaan before me – "

"Who was a young girl, and strong, my sister's child," Mutsak broke in. "Strong-hipped for children was Kasaan, and straight-legged and quick of foot. She made better moccasins than any of all the young girls, and the bark-rope she braided was the stoutest. And she had a smile in her eyes, and a laugh on her lips; and her temper was not hasty, nor was she unmindful that men give the law and women ever obey."

"As I say, I was very sick," Lone Chief went on. "And when my father, the Otter, brought the girl Kasaan before me, I said rather should they make me ready for burial than for marriage. Whereat the face of my father went black with anger, and he said that I should be served according to my wish, and that I who was yet alive should be made ready for death as one already dead – "

"Which be not the way of our people, O White Man," spoke up Mutsak. "For know that these things that were done to Lone Chief it was our custom to do only to dead men. But the Otter was very angry."

"Ay," said Lone Chief. "My father, the Otter, was a man short of speech and swift of deed. And he commanded the people to gather before the lodge wherein I lay. And when they were gathered, he commanded them to mourn for his son who was dead – "

"And before the lodge they sang the death-song – *O-o-o-o-o-o-a-haa-ha-a-ich-klu-kuk-ich-klu-kuk,*" wailed Mutsak, in so excellent an imitation that all the tendrils of my spine crawled and curved in sympathy.

"And inside the lodge," continued Lone Chief, "my mother blackened her face with soot, and flung ashes upon her head, and mourned for me as one already dead; for so had my father commanded. So Okiakuta, my mother, mourned with much noise, and beat her breasts and tore her hair; and likewise Hooniak, my sister, and Seenatah, my mother's sister; and the noise they made caused a great ache in my head, and I felt that I would surely and immediately die.

"And the elders of the tribe gathered about me where I lay and discussed the journey my soul must take. One spoke of the thick and endless forests, where lost souls wandered crying, and where I, too, might chance to wander and never see the end. And another spoke of the big rivers, rapid with bad water, where evil spirits shrieked and lifted up their formless arms to drag one down by the hair. For these rivers, all said together, a canoe must be provided me. And yet another spoke of the storms, such as no live man ever saw, when the stars rained down out of the sky, and the earth gaped wide in many cracks, and all the rivers in the heart of the earth rushed out and in. Whereupon they that sat by me flung up their arms and wailed loudly; and those outside heard, and wailed more loudly. And as to them I was as dead, so was I to my own mind dead. I did not know when, or how, yet did I know that I had surely died.

"And Okiakuta, my mother, laid beside me my squirrel-skin parka. Also she laid beside me my parka of caribou hide, and my raincoat of seal gut, and my wet-weather muclucs, that my soul should be warm and dry on its long journey. Further, there was mention made of a steep hill, thick with briers and devil's-club, and she fetched heavy moccasins to make the way easy for my feet.

"And when the elders spoke of the great beasts I should have to slay, the young men laid beside me my strongest bow and straightest arrows, my throwing-stick, my spear and knife. And when the elders spoke of the darkness and silence of the great spaces my soul must wander through, my mother wailed yet more loudly and flung yet more ashes upon her head.

"And the girl, Kasaan, crept in, very timid and quiet, and dropped a little bag upon the things for my journey. And in the little bag, I knew, were the flint and steel and the well-dried tinder for the fires my soul must build. And the blankets were chosen which were to be wrapped around me. Also were the slaves selected that were to be killed that my soul might have company. There were seven of these slaves, for my father was rich and powerful, and it was fit that I, his son, should have proper burial. These slaves we had got in war from the Mukumuks, who live down the Yukon. On the morrow, Skolka, the shaman, would kill them, one by one, so that their souls should go questing with mine through the Unknown. Among other things, they would carry my canoe till we came to the big river, rapid with bad water. And there being no room, and their work being done, they would come no farther, but remain and howl for ever in the dark and endless forest.

"And as I looked on my fine warm clothes, and my blankets and weapons of war, and as I thought of the seven slaves to be slain, I felt proud of my burial and knew that I must be the envy of many men. And all the while my father, the Otter, sat silent and black. And all that day and night the people sang my death-song and beat the drums, till it seemed that I had surely died a thousand times.

"But in the morning my father arose and made talk. He had been a fighting man all his days, he said, as the people knew. Also the people knew that it were a greater honour to die fighting in battle than on the soft skins by the fire. And since I was to die anyway, it were well that I should go against the Mukumuks and be slain. Thus would I attain honour and chieftainship in the final abode of the dead, and thus would honour remain to my father who was the Otter. Wherefore he gave command that a war party be made ready to go down the river. And that when we came upon the Mukumuks I was to go forth alone from my party, giving semblance of battle, and so be slain."

"Nay, but hear, O White Man!" cried Mutsak, unable longer to contain himself. "Skolka, the shaman, whispered long that night in the ear of the Otter, and it was his doing that Lone Chief should be sent forth to die. For the Otter being old, and Lone Chief the last of his sons, Skolka had it in mind to become chief himself over the people. And when the people had made great noise for a day and a night and Lone Chief was yet alive, Skolka was become afraid that he would not die. So it was the counsel of Skolka, with fine words of honour and deeds, that spoke through the mouth of the Otter."

"Ay," replied Lone Chief. "Well did I know it was the doing of Skolka, but I was unmindful, being very sick. I had no heart for anger, nor belly for stout words, and I cared little, one way or the other, only I cared to die and have done with it all. So, O White Man, the war party was made ready. No tried fighters were there, nor elders, crafty and wise – naught but five score of young men who had seen little fighting. And all the village gathered together above the bank of the river to see us depart. And we departed amid great rejoicing and the singing of my praises. Even thou, O White Man, wouldst rejoice at sight of a young man going forth to battle, even though doomed to die.

"So we went forth, the five score young men, and Mutsak came also, for he was likewise young and untried. And by command of my father, the Otter, my canoe was lashed on either side to the canoe of Mutsak and the canoe of Kannakut. Thus was my strength saved me from the work of the paddles, so that, for all of my sickness, I might make a brave show at the end. And thus we went down the river.

"Nor will I weary thee with the tale of the journey, which was not long. And not far above the village of the Mukumuks we came upon two of their fighting men in canoes, that fled at the sight of us. And then, according to the command of my father, my canoe was cast loose and I was left to drift down all alone. Also, according to his command, were the young men to see me die, so that they might return and tell the manner of my death. Upon this, my father, the Otter, and Skolka, the shaman, had been very clear, with stern promises of punishment in case they were not obeyed.

"I dipped my paddle and shouted words of scorn after the fleeing warriors. And the vile things I shouted made them turn their heads in anger, when they beheld that the young men held back, and that I came on alone. Whereupon, when they had made a safe distance, the two warriors drew their canoes somewhat apart and waited side by side for me to come between. And I came between, spear in hand, and singing the war-song of my people. Each flung a spear, but I bent my body, and the spears whistled over me, and I was unhurt. Then, and we were all together, we three, I cast my spear at the one to the right, and it drove into his throat and he pitched backward into the water.

"Great was my surprise thereat, for I had killed a man. I turned to the one on the left and drove strong with my paddle, to meet Death face to face; but the man's second spear, which was his last, but bit into the flesh of my shoulder. Then was I upon him, making no cast, but pressing the point into his breast and working it through him with both my hands. And while I worked, pressing with all my strength, he smote me upon my head once and twice, with the broad of his paddle.

"Even as the point of the spear sprang out beyond his back, he smote me upon the head. There was a flash, as of bright light, and inside my head I felt something give, with a snap – just like that, with a snap. And the

weight that pressed above my eyes so long was lifted, and the band that bound my brows so tight was broken. And a great gladness came upon me, and my heart sang with joy.

"This be death, I thought; wherefore I thought that death was very good. And then I saw the two empty canoes, and I knew that I was not dead, but well again. The blows of the man upon my head had made me well. I knew that I had killed, and the taste of the blood made me fierce, and I drove my paddle into the breast of the Yukon and urged my canoe toward the village of the Mukumuks. The young men behind me gave a great cry. I looked over my shoulder and saw the water foaming white from their paddles – "

"Ay, it foamed white from our paddles," said Mutsak. "For we remembered the command of the Otter, and of Skolka, that we behold with our own eyes the manner of Lone Chief's death. A young man of the Mukumuks, on his way to a salmon trap, beheld the coming of Lone Chief, and of the five score men behind him. And the young man fled in his canoe, straight for the village, that alarm might be given and preparation made. But Lone Chief hurried after him, and we hurried after Lone Chief to behold the manner of his death. Only, in the face of the village, as the young man leaped to the shore, Lone Chief rose up in his canoe and made a mighty cast. And the spear entered the body of the young man above the hips, and the young man fell upon his face.

"Whereupon Lone Chief leaped up the bank, war-club in hand and a great war-cry on his lips, and dashed into the village. The first man he met was Itwilie, chief over the Mukumuks, and him Lone Chief smote upon the head with his war-club, so that he fell dead upon the ground. And for fear we might not behold the manner of his death, we too, the five score young men, leaped to the shore and followed Lone Chief into the village. Only the Mukumuks did not understand, and thought we had come to fight; so their bow-thongs sang and their arrows whistled among us. Whereat we forgot our errand, and fell upon them with our spears and clubs; and they being unprepared, there was great slaughter – "

"With my own hands I slew their shaman," proclaimed Lone Chief, his withered face a-work with memory of that old-time day. "With my own hands I slew him, who was a greater shaman than Skolka, our own shaman. And each time I faced a man, I thought, 'Now cometh Death;' and each time I slew the man, and Death came not. It seemed the breath of life was strong in my nostrils and I could not die – "

"And we followed Lone Chief the length of the village and back again," continued Mutsak. "Like a pack of wolves we followed him, back and forth, and here and there, till there were no more Mukumuks left to fight. Then we gathered together five score men-slaves, and double as many women, and countless children, and we set fire and burned all the houses and lodges, and departed. And that was the last of the Mukumuks."

"And that was the last of the Mukumuks," Lone Chief repeated exultantly. "And when we came to our own village, the people were amazed at our burden of wealth and slaves, and in that I was still alive they were more amazed. And my father, the Otter, came trembling with gladness at the things I had done. For he was an old man, and I the last of his sons. And all the tried fighting men came, and the crafty and wise, till all the people were gathered together. And then I arose, and with a voice like thunder, commanded Skolka, the shaman, to stand forth – "

"Ay, O White Man," exclaimed Mutsak. "With a voice like thunder, that made the people shake at the knees and become afraid."

"And when Skolka had stood forth," Lone Chief went on, "I said that I was not minded to die. Also, I said it were not well that disappointment come to the evil spirits that wait beyond the grave. Wherefore I deemed it fit that the soul of Skolka fare forth into the Unknown, where doubtless it would howl for ever in the dark and endless forest. And then I slew him, as he stood there, in the face of all the people. Even I, Lone Chief, with my own hands, slew Skolka, the shaman, in the face of all the people. And when a murmuring arose, I cried aloud – "

"With a voice like thunder," prompted Mutsak.

"Ay, with a voice like thunder I cried aloud: 'Behold O ye people! I am Lone Chief, slayer of Skolka, the false shaman! Alone among men have I passed down through the gateway of Death and returned again. Mine eyes have looked upon the unseen things. Mine ears have heard the unspoken words. Greater am I than Skolka, the shaman. Greater than all shamans am I. Likewise am I a greater chief than my father, the Otter. All his days did he fight with the Mukumuks, and lo, in one day have I destroyed them all. As with the breathing of a breath have I destroyed them. Wherefore, my father, the Otter, being old, and Skolka, the shaman, being dead, I shall be both chief and shaman. Henceforth shall I be both chief and shaman to you, O my people. And if any man dispute my word, let that man stand forth!'

"I waited, but no man stood forth. Then I cried: 'Hoh! I have tasted blood! Now bring meat, for I am hungry. Break open the caches, tear down the fish-racks, and let the feast be big. Let there be merriment, and songs, not of burial, but marriage. And last of all let the girl Kasaan be brought. The girl Kasaan, who is to be the mother of the children of Lone Chief!'

"And at my words, and because that he was very old, my father, the Otter, wept like a woman, and put his arms about my knees. And from that day I was both chief and shaman. And great honour was mine, and all men yielded me obedience."

"Until the steamboat came," Mutsak prompted.

"Ay," said Lone Chief. "Until the steamboat came."

Land of the Good Shadows (1940), from
which "Left Behind" is taken, records the
biography of the Eskimo woman Anauta
as it was told to an American, Heluiz
Chandler Washburne (1892-   ). The
two women met in Winnetka, Illinois,
where Anauta was trying to support
herself by giving talks to school children
about her early life on Baffin Island at the
turn of the century.

Anauta's mother, Alea, was an Eskimo
woman; her father, George Ford, the
manager of a small trading post, was of
Eskimo-English background. The couple
had two sons and looked forward to the
birth of a daughter, but when the child
was born she was given up voluntarily to
the care of an old woman, Oomiálik.
Oomiálik's son had perished a few days
earlier when the ice pan on which he was
hunting walrus had been blown out to sea
and the old woman wished to give the
newborn child the lost hunter's name,
Anauta. In this way, according to Eskimo
belief, his spirit would have a chance to
live on earth again. As Oomiálik's foster
daughter, Anauta grew up in a group of
nomadic hunters dominated by the
brothers, Shemegak and Tuklavik. The
precariousness of their life is well
illustrated in "Left Behind".

Writing to Mrs. Washburne about the
reminiscences that were to be published as
Land of the Good Shadows, Anauta said,
"You know, Anauta Book to me is not just
a book. It's all my life, the lives of all my
most loved people, my own inmost
feelings and thoughts. In it I live once
more my whole childhood and the
happiest years of my life – also my most
bitter."

Other books resulting from their
collaboration are *Children of the Blizzard*
(1952) and *Wild Like the Foxes: The True
Story of an Eskimo Girl* (1956).

Left Behind

Heluiz Chandler Washburne and Anauta

The gray fall days were once more casting their dismal shadows over the summer gaiety of the people. The inland lakes and rivers were frozen but in the open harbor the water was yet black and forbidding. Waiting for the heavy snows when they could build their winter igloos, families everywhere were still living in their drafty skin tents.

In summer, tent dwelling was pleasant. The sun shone through the translucent skins with a soft yellow glow; one could see to work and be comfortable. But at this melancholy season, it was dark and gloomy inside. The flickering lamp did not light up the tent as it did the white walls of the igloo. One's hands were too cold for fine sewing and there was nothing to do but braid sinew, make fish line, or repair one's spears.

Certain characteristic weather changes were to be expected at this time of year. There were blustery days when the wind beat against the tents and shrilled through the open seams. But these storms quickly blew themselves out. It was the still calm days that people dreaded – those gray days before the real frost set in – when the smothering snow fell silently and the air was bleak and dead. No wind ruffled the ominous black water then, or stirred the heavy downward fall of snowflakes. Thicker and faster they came, smoothing out the landscape, piling up on the surface of the inky water in patches of floating mush. Shut in by the muffling grayness, one could see no signs of life. Even the water and sky were obscured. But through the prevailing stillness one could hear the quack of the eider ducks far out in the bay, or the splash of a seal and the faint breathing sound as he blew and went down again.

Everyone knew then that a real storm was on its way. As if affected by the quietness around them the people themselves became more silent. There was no desire to talk and be merry. Those who should have been out hunting sat in the tents smoking, and talked of what they were *going* to do when bad weather let up. People got in each other's way, and nerves were tense. Even the children became cross and fretful. They huddled together in the fur blankets and tried to warm their cold hands by the lamp. Occasionally they went outdoors to kick around in the dry feathery snow, but it was dreary play and they soon returned.

Not knowing how soon they could hunt again, people had to conserve their food, so they were hungry. Occasionally one of the more courageous men would venture out in his kayak after ducks or pigeons. If he was lucky enough to get a seal everyone rejoiced in fresh meat. But no one dared to go far out for the weather change came suddenly. When the drifting began one must be able to reach the shore quickly.

For several days the snow would silently pile higher and higher around the huddled tents. Then, without warning, would come the wind, screeching as it tore across the vast white expanses. The men would hurry outside, and carry their kayaks high on the beach, turning them bottoms up and weighting them down with stones. Shemegak would do the same with his oomiak. For three or four days then the snow would drift incessantly while the fierce wind beat it down hard, packing it firmly. Shivering and hungry, the people would sit in their tents waiting for the wind to spend itself. When it was over they would go outside and cut the snow-blocks to build their igloos, happy that the time had come when they could fold up their tents and enjoy the comfort of winter snowhouses. When three or four of these prolonged storms had come and gone, the weather usually cleared, the air was dry and frosty, the harbor froze up, and winter had really begun.

After one such late fall storm Shemegak suggested that now with firm snow on the ground the team could be used. It was a good season to travel inland to the fishing lakes. Everyone was tired of living on seal meat. A change of food would be welcome. Since the end of the cruising season Shemegak and Tuklavik had remained on the coast with their families, waiting for the winter snows. Anauta had stayed with them. But now she was glad to move on. Without more delay, preparations were made for departure. Kayaks and oomiak were left behind. The dog teams were harnessed, the three sledges loaded, and the party started off joyously. There were Shemegak and Tuklavik and their families, Supeali and her father, Anauta, and several young men who had joined the sons, Che-mang-nek and Puk-sauk. The three girls were in high spirits, chattering continually as they ran beside the dogs, jumping on and off the komotiks. The young men, too, were gay, and the air rang with their laughter. All were looking forward to good hunting and fishing and enough to eat.

They traveled rapidly, stopping to rest only during the short period of semi-darkness which occurred each day just before the long night began and the Northern Lights appeared. If the weather was thick, travel at these times was dangerous, especially over unfamiliar terrain – a whole team might drop over a cliff that no one could see. For three days they ran with their dogs; three times they made their snowhouses and slept. The last day they decided not to make camp but to push on in the beautiful clear night and reach the lake. The air was frosty and the runners of the sledge squeaked on the snow. The gray daylight passed, the moon appeared, round and golden. It was a perfect night for the Northern Lights – clear and cold – and everyone watched the heavens. Slowly a glimmer of light spread itself between them and the sky – like a golden blanket. In the deep blue on either side shone the piercing white fires of countless stars. As night progressed the lights became more splendid, rolling out great banners of rose and yellow. There was no wind to tear them into streamers of flaming color, to send them twisting and swaying across the heavens, so they lay still and close. Brighter and heavier they grew, hanging so low that Anauta felt she must reach up and touch the shining wonder. And the old familiar feeling of awe crept over her. She thought how Oomiálik had always loved to travel under the Good Shadows. Yes, Oomiálik was right, they proved the existence of a good spirit – no man could put Tak-ga-seát in the sky. They had been placed there to help the Eskimo, not only to illumine his way but to give him energy to endure the biting wind and difficult going. A lone wolf howled, but with the magic of the Good Shadows around them, even this dismal sound caused no distress. Merrily the group traveled ahead. It was only when the lights began to fade in the sky that they felt less like moving on. Reaching the lower end of the large lake the five young men decided to remain there and try their luck fishing. The others proceeded as planned to the upper end and made camp.

Che-mang-nek's mother, Tak-chek, was making him a new suit for the winter – a long-haired deerskin suit which would be warmer than the one he had been wearing all summer. Each evening when camp was made she sewed on it. Che-mang-nek must have it before more big winds and bad weather came on. Angmak, Anauta, and Supeali promised her that when it was finished they would take it down to Che-mang-nek at the boys' camp. This would be an adventure and they made many plans for the trip. Angmak and Anauta were going to wear their new suits, with the black sealskin fronts, and show the boys how fine they looked.

The families had been at the lake four or five sleeps when those well versed in weather signs began to cast uneasy glances at the sky. The clouds were a strange brassy color – bad weather was brewing. All that day Tak-chek stayed in to work on the suit. All that night, too, she sat up sewing.

The next morning she announced that the suit was finished. Che-mang-nek must have his warm clothes that day. Tomorrow the storm might break. Now the girls were in a predicament. They had promised to deliver the suit as soon as it was finished. But not realizing that it would be completed so quickly, Anauta had already promised Tuklavik to assist him in cutting fish holes. Angmak and Supeali had also agreed to help some of the other men. However, deciding it was more important to carry the suit than to chisel holes and haul away broken ice, they asked to be let off from these tasks.

Angmak and Supeali were successful in winning their release, but when Anauta asked Tuklavik, he replied firmly that there was no use in all three going. They would only play on the way and waste time. Angmak and Supeali could go together. Anauta would stay home and help him with the fishing. The girls were downcast. Anauta begged Tuklavik to change his mind. She could cut holes tomorrow; besides, permission to go had been promised. Supeali coaxed with all her prettiest wiles. Angmak, more outspoken, declared Tuklavik was not being fair. But Tuklavik was unmoved. "Two is enough," he said. For the first time in her life, Anauta was in real rebellion against Tuklavik. She was even inclined to disobey him and go anyway, but the habit of obedience was too strong.

Tuklavik gave his instructions then. Angmak and Supeali were to go immediately and come back without delay. They were not to sleep out. A storm was on its way. They had better hurry. With this he turned and walked away. Reluctantly Anauta followed, looking back at the two friends going without her. With a pang she noticed that Angmak was wearing her beautiful coat with the black front.

"I want to go with you, Angmak!" she called.

"Never mind, Anauta," Angmak answered cheerily. "We'll go together next time."

Supeali shouted that they would come home early and all go sliding in the moonlight. How often they had indulged in that forbidden sport, sitting on their coat tails and sliding down the hill out onto the frozen lake. So, laughing and happy, the girls passed out of sight.

Anauta helped Tuklavik cut the steps down through the hard-packed frozen snow that had drifted over the surface of this part of the lake, but frequently she glanced at the sky with apprehension. It grew more brassy, and yellow streaks appeared. The older people too seemed worried. No wind was blowing but from time to time a light gust of air struck their faces, first from one direction, then from another – an omen of approaching storm. The stillness was also a cause for alarm. The day wore on and Anauta's concern increased. Would Angmak and Supeali reach home before the storm broke?

Tuklavik and Anauta were still working busily, chipping through the thick ice for a fishing hole, when suddenly the drift swept down from the hills. Without warning they were enveloped in a smothering white blanket of whirling snow. Everything was blotted out. Their snowhouses were invisible. Tuklavik stopped chiseling and the deep hole was instantly filled with drifting snow.

"Tua-vi! We must get home before it is too late!" he said, and grabbing

Anauta's hand he started toward their igloos. But the wind was coming from that direction and they staggered against the drift, holding their arms before their bowed heads. Anauta could make no headway. The lashing gale blew her back, twisted her around. She stumbled and fell. Tuklavik, seeing that she was not strong enough to battle the fierce wind alone, put his strong arm across her shoulders as reinforcement. In this way they reached the houses, and stood for a moment beating the snow from their clothes before entering.

When Anauta had recovered her breath she spoke of her fear for Angmak and Supeali. The wind tore the words out of her mouth, but Tuklavik knew her thoughts. The girls had had time to reach the camp at the end of the lake, he assured her. Seeing the storm coming the boys would detain them till it was safe to return.

Entering the igloo Anauta noticed the anxious faces of those seated there. "Do you believe Angmak and Supeali are safe?" she asked, looking from one to another. Shemegak answered her. The storm had come early. His son, Che-mang-nek, would not let them start home in a storm. When the wind died down they would come. Reassured by these comforting words from one she loved and trusted, she returned to Tuklavik's house to wait.

The wind howled around the snowhouse. Anauta shuddered. Had the girls been there, they would have sat together on the soft furs, laughed and talked and not minded the storm. But they were gone. The roar of the gale filled her ears, and terror filled her heart.

Angmak's mother, Nea-hot-seak, sat silently in the corner, clasping and unclasping her hands. Puk-sauk's mother, Sher-he-neck, was also in the house, and the two wives tried to comfort each other, and to console themselves at the same time, with encouraging statements. But in their hearts the women were not convinced.

Several times Anauta went out into the blizzard to listen for some sound, to see if the weather showed signs of clearing. She struggled a few steps from the house but dared not go far lest she be unable to find her way back. The thick drifting snow beat into her eyes, her nose, and her ears, and she was thankful to return to the safety of the igloo.

The two fathers, Tuklavik and Aulamah, were sober, and heavy lines of worry creased their faces. Mercilessly they blamed themselves for having permitted their daughters to make the trip alone when they knew a storm was coming. Then again and again they confidently affirmed that of course the boys would not permit the girls to start home that day. Nevertheless, they anxiously watched the weather. No one felt like talking; so they sat quietly smoking and waiting.

Finally Tuklavik, noticing Anauta's deep concern and her prolonged silence, spoke to her, forcing himself to be cheerful. She must crawl into her sleeping-bag, he said. Angmak and Supeali were in theirs by now down at the boys' camp. When they came home tomorrow he was going to tell them how she had worried, and they would laugh at her foolish fears.

Before following Tuklavik's suggestion Anauta felt impelled to make one more trip outdoors. It was drifting so hard she could scarcely breathe. Standing in the shelter of the snowhouse she listened intently. Every nerve in her body was strained to the hearing point. Above the noise of the storm she thought she heard a faint cry. She took a step forward but the gale beat her back. Again she paused to listen. But this time there was nothing. After all it was only the wind, she thought, only the wind whistling around the igloo. She stumbled back into the house.

As she lay in her sleeping-bag, warm and comfortable, she thought of her two friends. Since she had first made her home with Tuklavik, she and Angmak had slept side by side. She reached out now and touched the empty sleeping-bag. She closed her eyes but it was long before she slept.

With the first grayness of dawn people were stirring. Coming outside Anauta glanced anxiously at the sky. The weather was clearing; the girls could get home today. She looked around her – the whole scene had changed. Where all had been smooth yesterday, today there were huge mounds of drifted snow. Rocky cliffs, softly covered before, were now blown clear, and exposed their gray and jagged faces. People were busy digging away the drift that covered their igloos. The dogs, hearing signs of life, shook off the snow that had buried them all night, and stretched stiffly.

Tuklavik was organizing a party to go after the girls. While he stood talking, a young man was seen running toward them from the direction of the boys' camp. As he approached they recognized Puk-sauk. Without a word to anyone, and brushing past Anauta who stood in the tunneled entrance, he hurried into his father's house. Anauta, following, saw his anxious searching glance. Then such an expression of fear came into his eyes that for one suffocating moment her heart stopped beating.

Tuklavik entered the house then, and Puk-sauk turned to him. "Did Angmak and Supeali reach home?" he demanded. There was no answer from Tuklavik, only a groan, as he stood there looking at his son, stunned by the knowledge his question had brought. Angmak's mother bowed her head and covered her face with her hands. With a sigh Tuklavik pulled himself together. "Come," he said, "we must search for them." Stooping he left the house and the others followed.

Immediately people scattered out in the direction of the boys' camp. Anauta walked with Angmak's father and mother, but as she went along she kept saying to herself – this searching was not necessary; such a thing could never happen to Angmak and Supeali; they would yet come safely home. She had gone but a short distance when one of the men called and held up his hand, signaling that he had found something.

Dreading what she might see, Anauta walked slowly toward the small wind-swept mound of snow by which the man stood. She remembered something she had often heard, that when people were freezing to death they burrowed under the snow leaving a small place through which to breathe. The snow served as a blanket to keep them alive. Perhaps Angmak and Supeali had buried themselves so, and the rescuers would find them quite unharmed.

As she drew nearer, however, she gave a low cry and covered her eyes. Then she looked again. The two girls were not protected as she had hoped. Their huddled frozen figures were exposed, partly covered by the drifting snow. There they sat, Supeali clasped tight in Angmak's arms. Standing before them Anauta reconstructed the events of that bitter black night – their desperate struggle, their failing strength. They had called for help – that *was* their cry she had heard through the storm – but she had failed to go to their rescue. Finally they had given up hope, and alone in the night, had said their last words to each other. Tears streamed down Anauta's face. How could they have been so close and she not have sensed their need? Through her tears she noticed that Supeali was wearing Angmak's new coat with the black front. She knew what must have happened. Supeali, never as strong as Angmak, had grown cold and fearful. Angmak, in a last attempt to save her friend's life, had wrapped her in her own coat, comforted and protected her in her arms. Anauta could almost hear her say, "I am warm enough without this old coat. You take it, Supeali." But Angmak was experienced enough to realize she could not survive the night with only her inner coat. It was like Angmak, always giving abundantly of everything she had, and like Supeali too, timid, calling forth protection and affection to the last. The girls' faces were quite free of snow, and Anauta saw that Angmak had been crying, for frozen to her cheeks were tiny drops of ice. Only yesterday they had gone off, waving, and shouting promises of new adventures together. Anauta turned away and a sob swelled in her throat.

The men set to work then to lift out the bodies, frozen together so completely that they could not be separated. Just as they were, Tuklavik and Aulamah carried them to the entrance of Tuklavik's house and set them down outside. That day was one of grief such as Anauta had never experienced. Everyone was heartbroken by the sudden loss of these two girls who had played and worked with them, traveled and hunted with them, and whom they had known since babyhood.

Late that afternoon Angmak and Supeali were laid away on the hill where the wind had drifted the ground clear. A stone grave was built around them, and as they had died, so were they buried, one in the arms of the other. Anauta, standing there, remembered the day they had tattooed each other as a mark of eternal friendship, and she looked at the small blue marks on her arm. Angmak had joked about their never being separated, even by death – that somehow they would all die together. How nearly that had happened! To Anauta, looking at her companions for the last time, the picture was not complete. "I am left behind," she thought sorrowfully. "I should be there with you – the three of us still traveling on together."

Sir Charles G. D. Roberts (1860-1943) was born in Douglas, New Brunswick. After graduating from the University of New Brunswick in 1879, he earned his living as a teacher, editor, poet, novelist, and short story writer. For his first three stories, published in 1892, he received a total of $59 and the advice that he stick to poetry.

Nowadays he is best known for his realistic animal stories, a genre that he pioneered. His characters live in the sea, in the far North, and in the New Brunswick woods that he knew as a boy. They must compete with one another and with man in order to survive. Killing for food was seen by Roberts as a law of nature, for as a character in *The Heart of the Ancient Wood* exclaims, "They've all got to eat meat, sometimes, for nature don't stand much foolin' with her laws!...Oftentimes it's seemed to me all life was just like a few butterflies flitterin' over a graveyard."

When Roberts was criticized for making his animals' emotional responses too like those of humans, he replied that "any full presentation of an individual animal of one of the more highly developed species must depict certain emotions not altogether unlike those which a human being might experience under like conditions." This sensitive treatment marks many of Roberts's finest stories in such well-known books as *The Kindred of the Wild* (1902), *The Watchers of the Trails* (1904), *Thirteen Bears* (1947), *The Last Barrier and Other Stories* (1958), and *King of Beasts and Other Stories* (1967).

"Mothers of the North" from *More Kindred of the Wild* (1911) depicts both the beauty of the North and the unremitting struggle for survival. Vilhjalmur Stefansson, the Icelandic-Canadian explorer and ethnologist who made important scientific discoveries in the North between 1906 and 1928, once described the Arctic as "lifeless except for millions of caribou and foxes, tens of thousands of wolves and musk-oxen, thousands of polar bears, millions of birds, and billions of insects." The struggle for survival has become even more desperate in recent years than it was in the days of Roberts and Stefansson. Overhunting and the effects of pollution have so threatened wildlife in the Arctic that caribou herds are greatly reduced in number and such characteristic northern species as polar bears, musk-oxen, walruses, narwhal, and peregrine falcons are facing extinction. How long will it be until "the last whale, like the last man, (will) smoke his last pipe, and then himself evaporate in the final puff"?

Mothers of the North
Charles G. D. Roberts

It was in the first full, ardent rush of the Arctic spring.

Thrilling to the heat of the long, long days of unobstructed sun, beneath the southward-facing walls of the glaciers, the thin soil clothing the eternal ice burst into green and flowering life. In the sunward valleys brooks awoke, with a sudden filming of grass along their borders, a sudden passionate unfolding of starlike blooms, white, yellow, and blue. As if summoned from sleep by the impetuous blossoms, eager to be fertilized, came the small northern butterflies in swarms, with little wasp-like flies and beetles innumerable. Along the inaccessible ledges of the cliffs the auks and gulls, in crowded ranks, screamed and quarrelled over their untidy nests, or filled the air with wings as they flocked out over the grey-green, tranquil sea. The world of the north was trying to forget for a little the implacable savagery, the deathly cold and dark, of its winter's torment.

The great, unwieldly, grunting walruses felt it, too, and responded to it – this ardour of the lonely Arctic spring, astray in the wastes. On the ledges of a rocky islet, just off shore, the members of a little herd were sunning themselves. There were two old bulls and four cows with their sprawling lumps of calves. All were in good humour with each other, lying with heads or fore-flippers flung amicably across each other's grotesque bodies, and grunting, groaning, grumbling in various tones of content as the pungent sunlight tickled their coarse hides. All seemed without a care beneath the sky, except one of the old bulls. He, being on watch, held his great tusked and bewhiskered head high above his wallowing fellows, and kept eyes, ears, and nose alert for the approach of any peril. One of the unshapely, helpless-looking calves, with its mother, lay in a hollow of the rock, perhaps twenty feet back from the water's edge – a snug spot, sheltered from all winds of north and east. The rest of the herd were grouped so close to the water's edge that from time to time a lazy, leaden-green swell would come lipping up and splash them. The cubs had a tendency to flounder away out of reach of these chill douches; but their mothers were very resolute about keeping them close to the water.

Presently the little groups were enlarged by one. Another old bull, who had been foraging at the sea-bottom, grubbing up clams, star-fish, and oysters with his tusks, and crushing them in the massive mill of his grinders, suddenly shot his ferocious-looking head above the surface. For all his gross bulk, in the water he moved with almost the speed and grace of a seal. In a second he was at the rock's edge. Hooking his immense tusks over it, he drew himself up by the force of his mighty neck, flung forward a broad flipper, dragged himself out of the water, and flopped down among his fellows with an explosive grunt of satisfaction.

They were not, it must be confessed, a very attractive company, these uncouth sea-cattle. The adults were from ten to eleven feet in length, round and swollen-looking as hogsheads, quite lacking the adornment of tails, and in colour of a dirty yellow-brown. Sparse bristles, scattered over their hides in rusty patches, gave them a disreputable, moth-eaten look. Their short but powerful flippers were ludicrously splayed. They had the upper half of the head small, flat-skulled, and earless; while the lower half, or muzzle was enormously developed to support the massive, downward-growing tusks, twelve to fifteen inches in length. This grotesque enlargement of the upper jaw was further emphasized by the bristling growth of long stiff whiskers which decorated it, giving the wearer an air of blustering irascibility. As for the calves, their podgy little forms had the same overblown look as those of their parents, but their clean young hides were not so wrinkled, nor were they anywhere disfigured by lumps and scars. They were without tusks, of course, but the huge development of their muzzles, in preparation for the sprouting of the tusks, gave them a

truculent air that was ludicrously belied by the mildness of their baby eyes. They rolled and snuggled against the mountainous flanks of their mothers, who watched them with vigilant devotion. The calf that lay furthest inland, apart from the rest, was in some pain, and whimpering. That morning it had got a nasty prod in the shoulder from the horn of a passing narwhal, and the anxious mother was trying to comfort it, gathering it clumsily but tenderly against her side and coaxing it to nurse. The rest of the herd, for the moment, was utterly content with life; but the troubled mother was too much engrossed with her little one's complaints to notice how caressing was the spring sun.

Meanwhile, not far away was another mother who, in spite of the spring, was equally ill-content. Down to the shore of the mainland, behind the island, came prowling a lean white bear with a cub close at her heels. The narrow bay between island and mainland was full of huge ice-cakes swung in by an eddy of the tides. Many of these wave-eaten and muddied floes were piled up on the shore along tide-mark, and as their worn edges softened under the downpour of the sun, they crumbled and fell with small glassy crashes. Hither and thither among them stole the brave mother, hoping to find some dead fish or other edible drift of the sea. She had had bad hunting of late – the shoals of the salmon had been inexplicably delaying their appearance on the coast – and she was feeling the pangs of famine. To be sure, she was filling her stomach, after a fashion, with the young shoots of rushes and other green stuff, but this was not the diet which Nature had framed her for. And in her lack of right nourishment she was pouring her very life itself into her breasts, in the effort to feed her little one. He, too, was suffering, so scanty was the supply of mother's milk. Even now, as the great bear stopped to nose a mass of seaweed, the cub crowded under her flank, and began to nurse, whimpering with disappointment at the too thin stream he drew. Her fierce eyes filmed, and she turned her head far round in order to lick him tenderly.

The stranded ice-floes yielded nothing that a bear could eat, and she was ranging on down the shore, disconsolately, when all at once a waft of air drew in from seaward. It came direct from the island, and it brought the scent of walrus. She lifted her long black-edged muzzle and sniffed sharply, then stood as rigid as one of the ice-cakes, and searchingly scrutinized the island. The cub, either imitating his mother or obeying some understood signal, stood moveless also. One of the earliest lessons learned by the youngsters of the wild is to keep still.

There was not a walrus in sight, but the bear's nostrils could not deceive her. She knew the huge sea-beasts were there, on the other side of the island, and she knew they would be very much at ease on such a day as this, basking in the sun. Walruses were not the quarry she would have chosen. The great bulls, courageous and hot-tempered, the powerful cows, dauntless as herself in defence of their young – she knew them for antagonists to be avoided whenever possible. But just now she had no choice. Her cub was not getting food enough. To her there was nothing else in the world so important as that small, troublesome, droll-eyed, hungry cub.

Keeping herself now well out of sight behind the ice-floes, with the cub close at her heels, she stole down to the edge of the retreating tide. The bay was too crowded with slowly-moving floes to be quite as safe for the cub as she would have had it, but she could not leave him behind. She kept him close at her side as she swam. He was a good swimmer, diving fearlessly when she dived, his little black nose cutting the grey-green water bravely and swiftly. In everything he imitated her stealth, her speed, her vigilance, for he knew there was big game in this hunting.

The island was a ridge of some elevation, shelving down by ledges to the sea. The white bear knew better than to climb the ridge and try to steal down upon the walruses. She was well aware that they would be keenly on the watch against any approach from the landward side. From that direction came all they feared. When she arrived at the island, she swam along, close under shelter of the shore, till she reached the extremity. Then, behind the shelter of a stranded floe, she drew herself out, at the same time flattening herself to the rock till she seemed a part of it. Every movement the cub copied assiduously. But when she rose upon her haunches, and laid her narrow head in a cleft of the ice-flow to peer over, he kept himself in the background and watched her with his head cocked anxiously to one side.

The walruses were in full view, not fifty yards away. For all the pangs of her hunger, the mother bear never stirred, but remained for long minutes watching them, studying the approaches, while the scent of them came on the light breeze to her nostrils. She saw that the herd itself was inaccessible, being well guarded and close to the water. If she should try to rush them, they would escape at the first alarm; or if she should succeed in catching one of the cubs in the water, she would be overwhelmed in a moment – caught by those mighty tusks, dragged to the bottom, drowned and crushed shapeless. But with gleaming eyes she noted the cow and calf lying further up the slope. Here was her chance – a dangerous one enough, but still a chance. She dropped down at last to all fours, crouched flat, and began worming her way upward among the rocks, making a covert of the smallest hummock or projection. The cub still followed her.

It was miraculous how small the great white beast managed to make herself as she slowly crept up upon her quarry. Her movements were as noiseless as a cat's. They had need to be, indeed, for the hearing of the walrus is keen. There was not a sound upon the air but the heavy breathings and gruntings of the herd, and the occasional light tinkle and crash of crumbling ice.

At a distance of not more than twenty paces from the prey, the old bear stopped and gave a quick backward glance at her cub. Instantly the latter stopped also, and crouched warily behind a rock. Then his mother crept on alone. She knew that he was quite agile enough to avoid the floundering rush of any walrus, but with him she would take no risks.

Suddenly, as if some premonition of peril had smitten her, the mother walrus lifted her head and stared about her anxiously. There was no danger in sight, but she had grown uneasy. She lowered her head against her calf's plump flank, and started to push him down the slope toward the rest of the herd.

Not a dozen feet away, an enormous form, white and terrible, arose as if by magic out of the bare rocks. A bellow of warning came from the vigilant old bull down below. But in the same instant that white mass fell upon the cringing calf, and smashed its neck before it knew what was happening.

With a roar the mother walrus reared herself and launched her huge bulk straight forward upon the enemy. She was swift in her attack –

amazingly so – but the white bear was swifter. With astonishing strength and deftness, even in the moment of delivering that fatal blow, she had pushed the body of her prey aside, several feet up the slope. At the same time, bending her long back like a bow, she succeeded in evading the full force of the mother's assault, which otherwise would have pinned her down and crushed her. She caught, however, upon one haunch, a glancing blow from those descending tusks, which came down like pile-drivers, and a long red mark leapt into view upon her white fur. The next moment she had dragged the prey beyond reach of the frantic mother's next plunging charge.

The rocky slope was now in an uproar. The other cows had instantly rolled their startled young into the sea and were tumbling in after them with terrific splashing. The three bulls, grunting furiously, were floundering in great loose plunges up the slope, eager to get into the fray. The bereaved mother was gasping and snorting with her prodigious efforts, as she hurled herself in huge sprawling lunges after the slayer of her young. So agile was she proving herself, indeed, that the bear had enough to do in keeping out of her reach, while half lifting, half dragging the prize up the incline.

At last the body of the calf caught in a crevice, and the bear had to pause to wrench it free. It was for a moment only, but that moment came very near being her last. She felt rather than saw the impending mass of the cow as it reared itself above her. Like a spring suddenly loosed, she bounded aside, and those two straight tusks came down, just where she had stood, with the force of a ton of bone and muscle behind them.

Wheeling in a flash to follow up her advantage, the desperate cow reared again. But this time she was caught at a disadvantage. Her far more intelligent adversary had slipped around behind her, and now, as she reared, struck her a tremendous buffet on the side of the neck. Caught off her balance, the cow rolled down the slope, turning clear over before she could recover her footing. The three bulls, in the midst of their floundering charge up the hill, checked themselves for a moment to see how she had fared. And in that moment the bear succeeded in dragging her prize up a steep where the walruses could not hope to follow. A few yards more, and

52   Charles G. D. Roberts

she had gained a spacious ledge some twenty feet above the raging walruses. A second or two later, in answer to her summons, the cub joined her there, scrambling nimbly over the rocks at a safe distance from the foe.

Realizing now that the marauder had quite escaped their vengeance, the three bulls at length turned away, and went floundering and snorting back to the sea. The mother, however, inconsolable in her rage and grief, kept rearing herself against the face of the rock, clawing at it impotently with her great flippers, and striking it with her tusks till it seemed as if they must give way beneath the blows. Again and again she fell back, only to renew her futile and pathetic efforts the moment she could recover her breath. And from time to time the old bear, nursing the cub, would glance down upon her with placid unconcern. At last, coming in some sort to her senses, the unhappy cow turned away and crawled heavily, with a slow, jerky motion, down the slope. Slowly, and with a mighty splash, she launched herself into the sea, and swam off to join the rest of the herd a mile out from shore.

Yves Thériault (1915-   ) grew up in Montreal. After leaving school at fifteen, he supported himself in a variety of ways ranging from trapping, driving trucks, and selling cheese to writing scripts for the NFB and Radio-Canada. Over the last thirty-six years he has written more than twenty-five books published in Quebec in French. At least half a dozen of these have been translated into English, including *Agaguk* (1958), from which the following story is taken; *Ashini* (1960), a Governor General's Award winner; *N'tsuk* (1968); and *Agoak* (1979).

The hero of *Agaguk* is a young man who rejects the life of an Eskimo settlement in northern Quebec and who sets out with his wife, Iriook, to look for the promised land. Happiness, freedom, independence from his father, and a return to the lifestyle of his ancestors are associated with the tundra which provides the food, furs, and solitude necessary to his physical and psychological survival.

"The Furs" depicts the white man's habitual exploitation of the native. The trader McTavish has developed a barter system which inevitably favours the fur company and victimizes the trapper. On a previous occasion when Agaguk had been cheated by a trader, he had taken a terrible revenge, burning the man alive by setting fire to his tent. On the occasion described in the following story, he finds solace in alcohol.

In viewing traditional Eskimo society as pure and noble and the world of nature as paradisal and consoling, Thériault adopts a romantic attitude that was not uncommon in the nineteenth and early twentieth centuries. For example, Captain John Ross, who in 1818 was the first white man to encounter the most northerly of the Eskimos, described them as "*virtuous* savages". This attitude produced the paternalism that has been an aspect of native-white relationships since the nineteenth century.

The Furs*

Yves Thériault

Near the river, far from the village, Agaguk and Iriook followed their destiny. Now the woman's parka bulged in front. Her belly swelled. Within, the new life grew each day. And every night Iriook, in panic, implored the Spirits to make this weight in her a boy.

On the tundra, the wind grew sharp. In the morning it was cold and the frost covered the dark moss with whiteness. Sometimes the odor of snow came in the clear blue sky. Then Agaguk stood before the hut and scanned the north. One evening he said, "Tomorrow the snow will come."

And the next morning indeed the snow did come, first a gust of wind, a terrible driving wind. The snow came from the north, riding the wind. It was a white fluid wall, which darkened the world. Then everything was enveloped by the icy, dense flakes, hitting the skin like chick peas. Contrary to the usual course, everything was covered, buried in a few hours. When the wind let up and the pale sun returned, three days had gone by. The tundra had become again the snow plain, the polar vastness. Seven months of misery began, for the distracted and famished animals as well as for the men who would have to survive in this deceitful environment.

With this first new snow, Agaguk built his igloo. Then he transferred all they owned to it and took down the hut. "When will be your time?" he asked that evening. He had touched this belly that was like a balloon and that compelled the woman to walk awkwardly in the igloo.

"Surely three more months," said Iriook. "Surely three, maybe four. Why do you ask?"

*Translated by Miriam Chapin

"I was waiting for the snow," he said. "To barter the skins I have here –
we need salt, bullets – "

"I need some things too."

"A rifle for you," said Agaguk. "Yours is old."

"I don't need that."

"Yes, you might."

He was making calculations. "We lack a lot of things."

Iriook agreed. "When will you go?"

"Early tomorrow, with the dogs."

"And when will you be back?"

"It takes four days to go to the Company's village on the Big Water. Four
to return. I shall stay there one whole day."

She said nothing, but the look she turned on Agaguk was eloquent.
What would he do over there? What would happen to him?

"You've been to the Company's village before," she said. "What's it like
there? I've never been there, me." She felt brave enough to go with him,
even if the child within her was becoming a burden.

Agaguk raised his shoulders. "There's nothing there. The trading post,
the igloos, that's all. I'll be there only one day, maybe less...."

Iriook did not feel reassured. "There's nothing else?" she insisted.

"What do you expect?" Agaguk answered harshly.

At daybreak the next morning he harnessed the dogs and came near
Iriook, not knowing what to say. But he stood beside her and felt the
woman's hand rest on his arm. That had to suffice. "I'll be waiting," she
said. "Come home quickly."

A crack of the long whip, the man's shout, brought the dogs to their
feet, whining. The animals leaped in the traces at the second stroke of the
whip, broke the runners free and the outfit took off. The sled carried what
was needed to feed the dogs, and the fat, the ammunition, the bundle of
furs, the caribou skins in which Agaguk would roll himself for the night,
the igloo lamp and the pemmican.

Agaguk had slipped the long snow knife in his belt, the tool with which
to build a night's igloo, and another knife, shorter, to finish off and cut up
any game he might bring down along the way. How could he know what
would be the luck of the road?

Standing, one foot on each sled runner, he let himself be pulled along
by the dogs. The load was not heavy, for on his return he would have to

bring whatever he got in exchange. The surface was hard and compact, the sled glided along without difficulty, and the dogs ran willingly. Here on the tundra, the snow is not treacherous. The ground is even, without cracks. The snow piles up without faults, unlike that on the islands to the north, where in the polar ice abysses open up ready to swallow man and dog team together. The dogs have a nose for these dangers. The head dog can recognize the sure footing. He distrusts the hand's breadth crust of snow, barely covering a crevasse twenty meters deep. He goes around the danger and avoids it. But this makes necessary a zigzag course, sometimes a very slow one.

On the tundra there is none of that, but instead a rapid run in a straight line. It went so smoothly that Agaguk could hope to cover in three days a distance that formerly took him four to walk. But then he had a savage wind to fight, the snow was not frozen and crisp as it was now, just right for speed.

He let the dogs travel without a halt until evening. At first he had driven them hard, but after a while he decided that he would cover more ground before night if he let them take their own gait, and they would not be exhausted. The evening gray was showing in the east when he stopped.

The dogs were still frisky, though covered with ice. Agaguk undid his bundle and threw a frozen fish to each one, which they devoured instantly. They kept circling around him, hoping for another morsel, but he was not moved. He knew that a dog on the trail ought to eat only a little at a time and that he runs much better with an empty belly. Rationing thus had its usefulness, aside from lightening the load to draw, in making sure that the sled dogs would be eager. Disappointed in their hopes, they wandered aimlessly for a moment. The head dog and a jealous bitch fought a brief battle. Soon one of the dogs dug a hole in the snow, using his muzzle and his paws. He slid in to sleep, having created his own igloo to his own measure and for his own needs. The others did the same, one by one. In a few minutes they were all out of sight in their improvised burrows. Their warmth made the snow at the opening crumble, blocking the entrance and hiding it. A gust of wind spread a fine snow over all, and soon no trace of the dogs remained. They could sleep in peace, warm and in comfort.

In his turn Agaguk built an igloo, putting it together in a hurry and making it just big enough for himself. Tomorrow the wind would begin to pull it apart. He carried all the sled load inside, out of danger from wind, dogs and wolves, then he placed the stone lamp on the floor; it was a more primitive utensil than the metal stove that Iriook was so proud of. That stove, which the white man had thought up for Eskimo use, and sold at the Company store, was a sort of wick affair in which they burned the ordinary heavy impure oil distilled from animal fats or from the seal and whale blubber they hunted at sea.

In the cramped space of the igloo, the stone lamp, which also used the oil by means of a woven wick, was just as good as a stove and took up much less room. While the flame gave him warmth and light, Agaguk melted some snow in a pot and put the pemmican to boil. As soon as it was ready, he devoured it, then he let the liquid boil until it was reduced to tasteless bouillon. Having eaten and drunk, he took out his pipe and tobacco. He smoked peacefully, unmoving, letting himself soak in the damp, soft heat of the igloo, a heat that made him dull and sleepy. Then he laid one of the caribou skins on the ground, folded it in two and lay down, rolling himself in the other skin.

When he woke up in the morning, he was ready to resume his journey, every muscle relaxed, his energy renewed. It was another fine day, almost without wind, and the dogs could again run at their usual pace. As before, Agaguk traveled standing on the sled runners, except for a few moments at a time when he felt numbed. Then he ran alongside the outfit or behind it at the same rate as the animals. It took him three and a half days to reach the post.

It was a collection of a dozen grayish houses, with a few igloos on the edge. A radio antenna stuck up thirty meters in the air, a thin steel obelisk. At the entrance to the village, an enormous reservoir of heavy oil supplied heat to the houses, and near the Company warehouse a smaller building, from which came crackling noises, sheltered a diesel electric generator. That was all.

The monotony of these few buildings succeeded the desolation of the plain; they were no less desolate – in fact they made the desert seem more vast, they extended its boundaries. Here, in a blizzard, a man could go out merely to pass from one house to another, and without realizing it blunder off in the wrong direction, to be lost in the white turmoil and perish before he could be found. It happened often, and more than one white man living in the Arctic would not dare stick his nose outside during a blizzard unless for some desperate emergency. When the wind rose, driving a wall of snow before it, when this swirling, blinding, deadly mass came down on the post, there was nothing to do but to sit at home and wait for good weather to return. Only so could one survive....

In front of the Company's establishment, Agaguk tied his lead dog to the post planted there for the purpose. Then he took the heavy bundle of furs on his back and went into the store. There was no one there but the clerk, a tall, thin Scotsman, with reddish hair and a mournful, unhealthy face. He said nothing, gave no welcome when the Eskimo entered. His expression remained cool and watchful. He had glanced at the bundle, but that look betrayed no interest. He waited while Agaguk undid the straps and spread the skins on the floor. "I've come to trade my furs," said Agaguk.

The man nodded slowly. "The price of furs is very low," he said.

Agaguk shrugged. He had been hearing that for so many years. And others before him had been able to learn it by heart, so many times was it said and repeated. "Very low," the man said again in a lugubrious tone.

Agaguk lifted the first lot of furs, fifteen mink, almost all first-call. The man McTavish spread them out on the counter and examined them one by one. His look was brief, that of an expert. He knew how to discover the smallest rubbed spot, the bruise that spoiled the workable part of the skin. If it was summer fur or the velvety fur of winter, if it came from a healthy mink or a sick one, if the dressing had been done with care or not, McTavish would find out in the wink of an eye. He threw the inspected skins farther along the counter, the good to one side, the rejected ones to the other. But every time, no matter what Eskimo was concerned, the good skins were rare.

Agaguk watched the performance as it went on. He had a twist at the corner of his mouth, an odd look in his eye. He picked up one of the rejected skins. "What's the matter with this?"

McTavish smiled. He was used to protests. They did not affect him any more; he had exercised this ungrateful trade for twenty years. He pointed to a tiny scratch on the inside of the skin, where it was no more the back and not yet the belly. The scratch did not go through the leather. "Reject," he said.

Agaguk turned red. "It's nothing," he cried. "It doesn't hurt the fur – that's not enough!"

The Scotsman looked coldly at the Eskimo before him. Twenty years of this game, twenty years of this kind of talk, twenty centuries – he grabbed all the skins on the counter, rolled them up and held them out to Agaguk.

"Take your furs away. I don't argue."

Agaguk stood a long moment staring at those blue-green eyes, eyes which did not smile and perhaps had never known how to smile. Then he shrugged. "As you like," he said.

He put the skins back on the counter, in front of McTavish. With a sigh the factor unwrapped the bundle and put the skins in the same order as before. After that it went fast. He inspected what remained in silence, the summer mink, the wolf skins, two caribou hides which Agaguk could spare, twenty of fox, as many of badger, a few muskrats. Then the Scotsman added up the total.

It was small. Even less than Agaguk had hoped, allowing for the customary bargaining. But he must have foreseen it. The Company never paid the hoped for price, however low a man set it. It rarely happened that one could get a man-to-man trade, in liberty and frankness. The Company had a monopoly – no competitor.... Illegal opposition never lasted long. Where could be found the manufactured goods, if not in the Company stores? The factor fixed the price, one must accept his figures. He himself owed his promotion to the success of his bargaining. At the head office, he was judged and weighed in the balance according to the margin he could establish between the market value of the furs and the value he allowed the Eskimos. Besides, by the high mark-up put on the normal prices of the merchandise for sale, mark-up which reduced still further the value of what was brought for barter, the Company had the opportunity to write incredible profits in its books. Against a hydra of this kind, an infinitely powerful monster, what could Agaguk do? Agaguk or anybody else?

"What do you want?" asked McTavish.

Of course, no money. Trade was carried on for the most necessary objects, for everything and nothing in the store. Certain Eskimos hardly succeeded in covering their necessities. They gave up their furs for knick-knacks, things which were of no use to them and often valueless. Like children without any sense at all, they were seized by sudden desires which they could not control. When bad times came, they had nothing, they were defenceless. Like all the other factors who came before him, McTavish willingly let them waste the fruit of their painful hunting expeditions.

Agaguk, thinking for himself, had always bought carefully. Perhaps he was different from the other Eskimos, in some remote fibre of his being. Often he had longed for the mechanical toys, the childish trash. He would have liked many of the things in the store, but he had always chosen indispensable things, for which he had come especially to exchange his furs. He listed what he wanted. "A rifle," he said, counting on his fingers. "Some ammunition, twenty boxes. Cotton cloth for my wife, kerosene for the lamp."

The Scotsman put a rifle on the counter. It was a weapon of very ordinary quality, efficient enough but sold in town at a very low price. Beside it he laid the twenty boxes of ammunition, and a tin of kerosene. "Tobacco for my pipe," Agaguk went on. The tobacco came to join the rest. "Salt," continued Agaguk. "A whole sack." He pointed to a fifty-pound sack.

"Half," said McTavish. "No more."

Agaguk bent his head, his face bewildered. The Scotsman knew how much he normally used. He did not intend to let him have more than half a sack. Besides, the bill was paid. "Some cotton cloth," went on Agaguk, resigned. "An iron kettle like that one. A shovel, see, like the one hanging there."

"That's all," said McTavish. "Nothing more after the salt."

"What?"

"I said that's all. After the salt, no more."

"Hardly half," cried Agaguk. "I want a lot more things."

"Next time," McTavish cut him short. "Next time."

McTavish had not learned the game yesterday. He was used to it. Agaguk, not knowing how to count, could not guess that even at the arbitrary price allowed for the furs, the Scotsman had considerably lowered their trading value. He felt no remorse. The Eskimo was not going away with empty hands. He had a gun, bullets, things with which to hunt and to feed himself. He had salt with which to dress the skins and preserve them, oil for his stove and tobacco to smoke. He could do without the rest. A shovel? What on earth for? Cloth for his wife? What good would that do? Nothing useful, that was sure. And the kettle? Nonsense...

According to his way of thinking, everything was going well and the Eskimo was not harmed. McTavish felt no twinge of conscience. After all, Agaguk was not obliged to accept the conditions of the bargain. He could leave, take back the furs, refuse the price he had set. That Agaguk had no other place to sell did not bother the Scotsman at all. It was none of his business nor any fault of his. What could he do about it? He had laid down certain conditions which the Eskimo had definitely accepted. He felt at peace with himself.

The Eskimo gathered up his purchases and carried them out to the sled. He took an hour to pack the load, to feed the dogs, to choke down the rage in his heart which urged him to do something desperate, to take a terrible revenge. . . . Was it bearable that the white men must always have the last word? Always, without the Eskimo ever being able to defend himself? But to whom could he complain? The white men, were they not all-powerful, and their interests in these countries all too well protected? He felt his mind confused, he could hardly knot the thongs to hold the load on the sled. The dream of vengeance would not leave his mind, but along with it there rose within him a contrary sentiment, a neutralizing thought that little by little calmed his fury. Vengeance? But how? To go into the store, to strike, to kill? It would be futile, ridiculous even, for they would take him prisoner before he had gone thirty steps in flight. To tell McTavish what he thought of him? He might as well talk to a rock. Agaguk raged at the memory of the man's icy look, the complete indifference he showed openly. What good would talking with him do? It would mean bad days to come. To oppose McTavish could bring no good. The Scotsman would get even for any insult at the next bargaining session. He would remember the Eskimo, keep his face in mind, wait his hour for revenge patiently. Others had tried their luck, Agaguk remembered well. What had happened was still talked about in the igloos. Okarnak had been the latest victim. Now he had to travel three weeks every year to trade his furs at a post farther away than the one that employed McTavish. For Okarnak that was the only way to obtain, if not justice, at least conditions equal to those which McTavish imposed on him before he started to take his revenge.

Nevertheless, outside, in front of the post, Agaguk knew that he could not go home to his igloo like this. Too many contradictory feelings were boiling in his breast. The need to escape somehow grew and grew, demanding immediate satisfaction. He did not identify his desires, he simply took account of their existence and recognized their strength. But in this isolated and inhospitable village, what way of escape could there be?

Under his parka Agaguk touched the beautiful shining mink pelt hidden there, the one that he still kept as his last reserve, which he had not considered offering McTavish to complete his transaction with him. He thought for a moment of going back to McTavish, of offering him this skin, truly a magnificent one, in return for the things he lacked, the kettle, the shovel, the cotton cloth he wanted to bring as a gift for Iriook. He thought of obtaining justice, this time, of insisting, of showing his independence as McTavish had done. But he changed his mind.

The mink skin would bring much more than those objects, which now he no longer wanted so very much, and which Iriook could certainly do without. More than the cloth, the shovel, the pot – something indefinable, this need to escape was suddenly made attainable by the presence of this forgotten bit of fur. He wanted to make some extraordinary gesture, to do something far outside his usual way of life, something that would mark the instant precisely, and for a long time.

Little by little he envisaged this escape, made it clear. Quickly he understood what he had to do. Between that unpleasant moment with McTavish, and his arrival at the igloo where Iriook would be waiting, something must happen, there must be a hiatus. He could not resume his journey, he could not return immediately to his wife. He whipped up his dogs; he felt a sudden lift in his spirits, an enthusiasm he did not try to control; he had made his decision, he knew what he would do. He drove the team straight to an igloo on the outskirts of the village, an igloo larger than the others, topped by a short mast where a tattered flag waved in the wind. It was a place well known to the Eskimos who passed the word to each other that there a man could satisfy his wants.

Did this igloo enjoy some special protection? Did the authorities shut their eyes to what went on there? Neither Agaguk nor the other Eskimos coming to trade could have said. They knew of its existence, they knew what they would find there.

Once within, Agaguk was brief. He displayed the mink pelt, the choicest of furs. The man who had received him, a half-breed Eskimo and Ojibway, was a trader well known all through the Arctic, who carried on his traffic under the nose of the RCMP. He examined the skin contemptuously.

"You kidding me?"

Here Agaguk felt more sure of himself. He snatched the skin out of the man's hands. "I'll go somewhere else," he said.

This time the threat made sense. He could go somewhere else. A white man in the same village, he said to himself, could fill his needs. The trader shook his head, grimaced. "The price of fur is down," he said.

"It's worth what it's worth."

"One bottle, that's all."

He reached into a cupboard behind him and took out a small bottle of liquor without a label, a syrupy white alcohol, distilled from some filthy mixture, brought there illegally. Agaguk began to stuff the mink skin under his parka. "No," he said.

They were sitting on the ground, their legs folded, and they argued in the flickering light of a little kerosene lamp. A frightful smell of rancid sweat, rotten grease and bad alcohol pervaded the igloo.

"Four bottles or nothing," said Agaguk. The man sighed. The palaver was going according to the rules. He would do well enough out of it, he knew. He took another bottle from the case.

The trader stared at the fur, the beautiful supple mink skin. He knew its worth. The Company would never see the color of it. Surreptitiously, as the liquor came in, someone would undertake to dispose of it. The beautiful skin would end up with some dishonest buyer in town. There was always somebody to buy unstamped skins. Later it would find its way to Europe. At the going price of mink, the risk was worth while. "Four bottles," Agaguk repeated firmly.

The man swore vulgarly in the white man's language, but he ended by taking two more bottles from the case and holding them out to Agaguk in exchange for the fur.

Agaguk left at once, bearing the precious flasks hidden under his parka. Outside, he jumped on the sled runners and whipped up the dogs. But he did not go very far over the snow plain. The hour to make camp had not yet come when he stopped his dogs and built an igloo.

He did not delay in carrying out his plan to escape. Feeding the dogs took only a moment, and then came the unloading of the sled, piling things safely in the igloo. Warm, sheltered, the dogs already buried under the snow, he lighted the stone lamp and instead of eating he quickly drank the first bottle. Though his body was not accustomed to alcohol, he nevertheless possessed such great physical strength that he hardly felt the effects of one dose. He drank the next one more slowly.

After a few minutes, he polished it off. His movements were slow and

he talked thickly to himself. He could hardly keep awake, but he still fought off his drowsiness. He could not have said what he was thinking. At first he had felt an airy lightness. He was visiting a marvellous country, a fairyland; his drunkenness was euphoria. After that stage, rage possessed him. Immense, domineering, it took hold of him, but before he could yield to his anger, he went to sleep. The alcohol in his veins had conquered all resistance.

In the morning he was sober, but he had a hangover and his head ached. He boiled a little pemmican and after he had eaten that he went out to feed his dogs which were yapping miserably. When he returned, he began to drink again, emptying the two remaining bottles. This time, drunkenness came more slowly. Since he had eaten, his body put up more resistance to the alcohol. He began to sing, a strange outcry without tune or meaning, a sort of animal howling. He beat time, striking his thigh with the palm of his hand. Outside the dogs began to howl in turn. The racket lasted a long time, but it died down, little by little. It was still light when Agaguk went to sleep, slouched against the sack of salt.

He woke at dawn the next day, with a thick mouth and a heavy head. Instinctively he measured out every movement, for each one hurt him. With infinite trouble he got to his feet and went out to feed his dogs. Most of the trip was still ahead of him. The wind was blowing hard and the sky was gray, snow was flying over the tundra. "Blizzard," he said to himself.

But he was not frightened and in spite of the physical ills that weighed on him, his mind and his thoughts were oddly clear. The episode with McTavish no longer made him ashamed; he didn't even care about it. It was over. The hiatus was filled in, he could now go back to Iriook.

Farley Mowat (1921-   ) is a colourful Canadian author and conservationist whose bushy beard and kilt are familiar sights in many parts of Canada, including Burgeo, a Newfoundland outpost where he lived for a time. He was born in Belleville, Ontario, but at the age of eight, he moved with his family to Saskatoon, Saskatchewan, where his father was to be the town's librarian. After serving in World War II and living in the Arctic for two years, Mowat began writing for a living in 1949.

In a recent interview, Mowat said, "I like to think I am a reincarnation of the Norse sagamen and, like them, my chief concern is with the tales of men and other animals, living under conditions of natural adversity." Among such stories are *The People of the Deer* (1952); *Lost in the Barrens* (1956); *Never Cry Wolf* (1963); *A Whale for the Killing* (1972); and *The Snow Walker* (1975), from which "Walk Well, My Brother" is taken.

Like Thériault, Mowat has a romantic attitude to native peoples. "Walk Well, My Brother" illustrates his belief that the Eskimo can teach the white man not only techniques of survival but also such moral values as patience, kindliness, and self-sacrifice.

Walk Well, My Brother

Farley Mowat

When Charlie Lavery first went north just after the war, he was twenty-six years old and case hardened by nearly a hundred bombing missions over Europe. He was very much of the new elite who believed that any challenge, whether by man or nature, could be dealt with by good machines in the hands of skilled men. During the following five years, flying charter jobs in almost every part of the arctic from Hudson Bay to the Alaska border, he had found no reason to alter this belief. But though his familiarity with arctic skies and his ability to drive trackless lines across them had become considerable, he remained a stranger to the land below. The monochromatic wilderness of rock and tundra, snow and ice, existed outside his experience and comprehension, as did the native people whose world this was.

One mid-August day in 1951 he was piloting a war-surplus Anson above the drowned tundra plains south of Queen Maud Gulf, homeward bound to his base at Yellowknife after a flight almost to the limit of the aircraft's range. The twin engines thundered steadily and his alert ears caught no hint of warning from them. When the machine betrayed his trust, it did so with shattering abruptness. Before he could touch the throttles, the starboard engine was dead and the port one coughing in staccato bursts. Then came silence – replaced almost instantly by a rising scream of wind as the plane nosed steeply down toward the shining circlet of a pond.

It was too small a pond and the plane had too little altitude. As Lavery frantically pumped the flap hydraulics, the floats smashed into the rippled water. The Anson careened wickedly for a few yards and came to a crunching stop against the frost-shattered rocks along the shore.

Lavery barely glanced at his woman passenger, who had been thrown into a corner of the cabin by the impact. He scrambled past her, flung open the door and jumped down to find himself standing knee deep in frigid water. Both floats had been so badly holed that they had filled and now rested on the rocky bottom.

The woman crawled to the door and Lavery looked up into an oval, warmly tinted face framed in long black hair. He groped for the few Eskimo words he knew:

Tingmeak ... *tokoiyo* ... smashed to hell! No fly! Understand?

As she stared back uncomprehending, a spasm of anger shook him. What a fool he'd been to take her aboard at all ... now she was a bloody albatross around his neck.

Four hours earlier he had landed in a bay on the Gulf coast to set out a cache of aviation gas for a prospecting company. No white men lived in that part of the world and Lavery had considered it a lucky accident to find an Eskimo tent pitched there. The two men who had run out to watch him land had been a godsend, helping to unload the drums, float them to tideline and roll them up the beach well above the storm line.

He had given each of them a handful of chocolate bars in payment for their work and had been about to head back for Yellowknife when the younger Eskimo touched his arm and pointed to the tent. Lavery had no desire to visit that squat skin cone hugging the rocks a hundred yards away and it was not the Eskimo's gentle persistence that prevailed on him – it was the thought that these Huskies might have a few white fox pelts to trade.

There were no fox pelts in the tent. Instead there was a woman lying on some caribou hides. *Nuliak* – wife – was the only word Lavery could understand of the Eskimo's urgent attempt at explanation.

The tent stank of seal oil and it was with revulsion that Lavery looked more closely at the woman. She was young and not bad looking – for a Husky – but her cheeks were flushed a sullen red by fever and a trickle of blood had dried at the corner of her mouth. Her dark eyes were fixed upon him with grave intensity. He shook his head and turned away.

T.B.... sooner or later all the Huskies got it... bound to the filthy way they lived. It would be no kindness to fly her out to the little hospital at Yellowknife already stuffed with dying Indians. She'd be better off to die at home....

Lavery was halfway back to the Anson before the younger Eskimo caught up with him. In his hands he held two walrus tusks, and the pilot saw they were of exceptional quality.

Ah, what the hell... no skin off my ass. I'm dead-heading anyhow....

"*Eeema.* Okay, I'll take your *nuliak.* But make it snappy. *Dwoee, dwoee!*"

While Lavery fired up the engines, the men carried the woman, wrapped in caribou-skin robes, and placed her in the cabin. The younger Eskimo pointed at her, shouting her name: Konala. Lavery nodded and waved them away. As he pulled clear of the beach he caught a glimpse of them standing in the slipstream, as immobile as rocks. Then the plane was airborne, swinging around on course for the long haul home.

Barely two hours later he again looked into the eyes of the woman called Konala ... wishing he had never seen or heard of her.

She smiled tentatively but Lavery ignored her and pushed past into the cabin to begin sorting through the oddments which had accumulated during his years of arctic flying. He found a rusty .22 rifle and half a box of shells, a torn sleeping bag, an axe and four cans of pork and beans. This, together with a small box of matches and a pocketknife in his stylish cotton flying jacket, comprised a survival outfit whose poverty testified to his contempt for the world that normally lay far below his aircraft.

Shoving the gear into a packsack he waded ashore. Slowly Konala followed, carrying her caribou robes and a large sealskin pouch. With mounting irritation Lavery saw that she was able to move without much difficulty. Swinging the lead to get a free plane ride, he thought. He turned on her.

"The party's over, lady! Your smart-assed boy friend's got you into a proper mess – him and his goddam walrus tusks!"

The words meant nothing to Konala but the tone was clear enough. She walked a few yards off, opened her pouch, took out a fishing line and began carefully unwinding it. Lavery turned his back on her and made his way to a ledge of rock where he sat down to consider the situation.

A thin tongue of fear was flickering in the back of his mind. Just what the hell *was* he going to do? The proper drill would be to stick with the Anson and wait until a search plane found him ... except he hadn't kept to his flight plan. He had said he intended to fly west down the coast to Bathurst before angling southwest to Yellowknife ... instead he'd flown a direct course from the cache, to save an hour's fuel. Not so bright maybe, considering his radio was out of kilter. There wasn't a chance in a million they'd look for him this far off-course. Come to that, he didn't even know exactly where he was ... fifty miles or so north of the Back River lakes would be a good guess. There were so damn few landmarks in this godforsaken country. ... Well, so he wasn't going to be picked up ... that left Shanks's mare, as the Limeys would say ... but which way to go?

He spread out a tattered aeronautical chart on the knees of his neat cotton pants. Yellowknife, four hundred miles to the southwest, was out of the question. ... The arctic coast couldn't be more than a hundred and fifty miles away but there was nobody there except a scattering of Huskies. ... How about Baker Lake? He scaled off the airline distance with thumb and forefinger, ignoring the innumerable lakes and rivers across the route. About two hundred miles. He was pretty fit ... should be able to manage twenty miles a day ... ten days, and presto.

Movement caught his eye and he looked up. Konala, a child-like figure in her bulky deerskin clothes, had waded out to stand on the submerged tail of a float. Bent almost double, she was swinging a length of line around her head. She let the weighted hook fly so that it sailed through the air to strike the surface a hundred feet from shore.

Well, there was no way she could walk to Baker. She'd have to stay put until he could bring help. His anger surged up again....Fishing, for God's sake! What in Jesus' sweet name did she think she was going to catch in that lousy little pond?

He began to check his gear. Lord, no *compass*... and the sun was no use this time of year. He'd never bothered to buy one of the pocket kind... no need for it... but there was a magnetic compass in the instrument panel of the old crate....

Lavery hurried back to the Anson, found some tools and went to work. He was too preoccupied to notice Konala haul in her line and deftly slip a fine char off the hook. He did not see her take her curved woman's knife and slice two thick fillets from the fish. The first he knew of her success was when she appeared at the open cabin door. She was so small that her head barely reached the opening. With one hand she held a fillet up to him while with the other she pushed raw pink flesh into her mouth, pantomiming to show him how good it was.

"Jesus, no!" He was revolted and waved her away. "Eat it yourself... you animal!"

Obediently Konala disappeared from the doorway. Making her way ashore she scraped together a pile of dry lichens then struck a light with flint and steel. The moss smoked and began to glow. She covered it with dwarf willow twigs, then spread pieces of the fish on two flat rocks angled toward the rising flames. When Lavery descended from the plane with the compass in his hand his appetite woke with a rush at the sight and smell of roasting fish. But he did not go near the fire. Instead he retreated to the rocks where he had left his gear and dug out a can of beans. He gashed his thumb trying to open the can with his pocketknife.

Picking up the axe, he pounded the can until it split. Raging against this wasteland that had trapped him, and the fate that had stripped him of his wings, he furiously shovelled the cold mess into his mouth and choked it down.

Konala sat watching him intently. When he had finished she rose to her feet, pointed northward and asked, *"Peehuktuk? We walk?"*

Lavery's resentment exploded. Thrusting his arms through the straps

of the packsack, he heaved it and the sleeping bag into position then picked up the rifle and pointed with it to the southwest.

"You're goddam right!" he shouted. "Me – *owunga peehuktak* that way! *Eeetpeet* – you bloody well stay here!"

Without waiting to see if she had understood, he began to climb the slope of a sandy esker that rose to the south of the pond. Near the crest he paused and looked back. Konala was squatting by the tiny fire seemingly unaware that he was deserting her. He felt a momentary twinge of guilt, but shrugged it off...no way she could make it with him to Baker, and she had her deerskins to keep her warm. As for food, well, Huskies could eat anything...she'd make out. He turned and his long, ungainly figure passed over the skyline.

With a chill of dismay he looked out across the tundra rolling to a measureless horizon ahead of him – a curving emptiness more intimidating than anything he had seen in the high skies. The tongue of fear began to flicker again but he resolutely shut his mind to it and stumbled forward into that sweep of space, his heavy flight boots slipping on rocks and sucking in the muskeg, the straps of the packsack already cutting into his shoulders through the thin cotton jacket.

There is no way of knowing what Konala was thinking as she saw him go. She might have believed he was going hunting, since that would have been the natural thing for a man to do under the circumstances. But in all likelihood she guessed what he intended – otherwise, how to explain the fact that ten days later and nearly sixty miles to the south of the downed plane, the sick woman trudged wearily across a waste of sodden muskeg to climb a gravel ridge and halt beside the unconscious body of Charlie Lavery?

Squatting beside him she used her curved knife to cut away the useless remnants of his leather boots, then wrapped his torn and bloody feet in compresses of wet sphagnum moss. Slipping off her parka, she spread it over his tattered jacket to protect him from the flies. Her fingers on his emaciated and insect-bitten flesh were tender and sure. Later she built a fire, and when Lavery opened his eyes it was to find himself under a rude skin shelter with a can of fish broth being pressed lightly against his lips.

There was a hiatus in his mind. Anxiously he raised himself to see if the aircraft was still on the pond, but there was no pond and no old Anson … only that same stunning expanse of empty plains. With a sickening lurch, memory began to function. The seemingly endless days of his journey flooded back upon him: filled with roaring clouds of mosquitoes and flies; with a mounting, driving hunger; the agony of lacerated feet and the misery of rain-swept hours lying shelterless in a frigid void. He remembered his matches getting soaked when he tried to ford the first of a succession of rivers that forever deflected his course toward the west. He remembered losing the .22 cartridges when the box turned to mush after a rain. Above all, he remembered the unbearable sense of loneliness that grew until he began to panic, throwing away first the useless gun, then the sodden sleeping bag, the axe … and finally sent him, in a heart-bursting spasm of desperation, toward a stony ridge that seemed to undulate serpent-like on the otherwise shapeless face of a world that had lost all form and substance.

Konala's face came into focus as she nudged the tin against his lips. She was smiling and Lavery found himself smiling weakly back at this woman who not so long before had roused his contempt and anger.

They camped on the nameless ridge for a week while Lavery recovered some of his strength. At first he could hardly bear to leave the shelter because of the pain in his feet. But Konala seemed always on the move: gathering willow twigs for fires, collecting and cooking food, cutting and sewing a new pair of boots for Lavery from the hides she had brought with her. She appeared tireless, but that was an illusion. Her body was driven to its many tasks only at great cost.

Time had telescoped itself so that Lavery would wake from sleep with shaking hands, hearing the engines of the Anson fail. It would seem to him that the plane had crashed only a few minutes earlier. It would seem that the terrible ordeal of his march south was about to begin again and he would feel a sick return of panic. When this happened, he would desperately fix his thoughts on Konala for she was the one comforting reality in all this alien world.

He thought about her a great deal, but she was an enigma to him. Sick as she was, how had she managed to follow him across those sodden plains and broken rock ridges ... how had she managed to keep alive in such a country?

After Konala gave him the completed skin boots carefully lined with cotton grass, he began to find answers to some of these questions. He was able to hobble far enough from camp to watch her set sinew snares for gaudy ground squirrels she called *hikik*, scoop suckers from a nearby stream with her bare hands, outrun snow geese that were still flightless after the late-summer moult and dig succulent lemmings from their peat bog burrows. Watching her, Lavery slowly came to understand that what had seemed to him a lifeless desert was in fact a land generous in its support of those who knew its nature.

Still, the most puzzling question remained unanswered. Why had Konala not stayed in the relative safety of the aircraft or else travelled north to seek her own people? What had impelled her to follow him ... to rescue a man of another race who had abandoned her?

Toward the end of their stay on the ridge, the sun was beginning to dip well below the horizon at night – a warning that summer was coming to an end. One day Konala again pointed north and, with a grin, she waddled duck-like a few paces in that direction. The joke at the expense of Lavery's splayed and painful feet did not annoy him. He laughed and limped after her to show his willingness to follow wherever she might lead.

When they broke camp, Konala insisted on carrying what was left of Lavery's gear along with her own pouch and the roll of caribou hides which was both shelter and bedding for them. As they trekked northward she broke into song – a high and plaintive chant without much melody which seemed as much part of the land as the fluting of curlews. When Lavery tried to find out what the song was all about, she seemed oddly reticent and all he could gather was that she was expressing kinship for someone or for some thing beyond his ken. He did not understand that she was joining her voice to the voice of the land and to the spirits of the land.

Retracing their path under Konala's tutelage became a journey of discovery. Lavery was forever being surprised at how different the tundra had now become from the dreadful void he had trudged across not long since.

He discovered it was full of birds ranging from tiny longspurs whose muted colouring made them almost invisible, to great saffron-breasted hawks circling high above the bogs and lakes. Konala also drew his attention to the endless diversity of tundra plants, from livid orange lichens to azure flowers whose blooms were so tiny he had to kneel to see them clearly.

Once Konala motioned him to crawl beside her to the crest of an esker. In the valley beyond, a family of white wolves was lazily hunting lemmings in a patch of sedge a hundred feet away. The nearness of the big beasts made Lavery uneasy until Konala boldly stood up and called to the wolves in their own language. They drew together then, facing her in a half circle, and answered with a long, lilting chorus before trotting away in single file.

Late one afternoon they at last caught sight of a splash of brilliant colour in the distance. Lavery's heartbeat quickened and he pushed forward without regard for his injured feet. The yellow-painted Anson *might* have been spotted by a search plane during their absence...rescue by his own kind might still be possible. But when the man and woman descended the esker to the shore of the pond, they found the Anson exactly as they had left it. There had been no human visitors.

Bitterly disappointed, Lavery climbed into the cockpit, seated himself behind the controls and slumped into black depression. Konala's intention of travelling northward to rejoin her own people on the coast now loomed as an ordeal whose outcome would probably be death during the first winter storm...if they could last that long. Their worn clothing and almost hairless robes were already barely adequate to keep the cold at bay. Food was getting harder to find as the birds left, the small animals began to dig in and the fish ran back to the sea. And what about fuel when the weather really began to turn against them?

Lavery was sullen and silent that evening as they ate their boiled fish, but Konala remained cheerful. She kept repeating the word *tuktu* –

caribou – as she vainly tried to make him understand that soon they would have the wherewithal to continue the journey north.

As the night wind began to rise he ignored the skin shelter which Konala had erected and, taking one of the robes, climbed back into the plane and rolled himself up on the icy metal floor. During the next few days he spent most of his time in the Anson, sometimes fiddling with the knobs of the useless radio, but for the most part morosely staring through the Plexiglass windscreen at a landscape which seemed to grow increasingly bleak as the first frosts greyed the tundra flowers and browned the windswept sedges.

Early one morning an unfamiliar sound brought him out of a chilled, nightmarish sleep. It was a muffled, subdued noise as of waves rolling in on a distant shore. For one heart-stopping instant he thought it was the beat of an aircraft engine, then he heard Konala's exultant cry.

"*Tuktoraikayai* – the deer have come!"

From the window of the dead machine Lavery looked out upon a miracle of life. An undulating mass of antlered animals was pouring out of the north. It rolled steadily toward the pond, split, and began enveloping it. The rumble resolved itself into a rattling cadence of hooves on rock and gravel. As the animals swept past, the stench of barnyard grew strong even inside the plane. Although in the days when he had flown high above them Lavery had often seen skeins of migrating caribou laced across the arctic plains like a pattern of beaded threads, he could hardly credit what he now beheld…the land inundated under a veritable flood of life. His depression began to dissipate as he felt himself being drawn into and becoming almost a part of that living river.

While he stared, awe-struck and incredulous, Konala went to work. Some days earlier she had armed herself with a spear, its shaft made from a paddle she had found in the Anson and its double-edged blade filed out of a piece of steel broken from the tip of the plane's anchor. With this in hand she was now scurrying about on the edge of the herd. The press was so great that individual deer could not avoid her. A snorting buck leapt high as the spear drove into him just behind the ribs. His dying leap carried him onto the backs of some of his neighbours, and as he slid off and disappeared into the ruck, Konala's blade thrust into another victim. She chose the fattest beasts and those with the best hides.

When the tide of caribou finally thinned, there was much work for Konala's knife. She skinned, scraped and staked out several prime hides destined for the making of clothes and sleeping robes, then turned her attention to a small mountain of meat and began slicing it into paper-thin sheets which she draped over dwarf willow bushes. When dry this would make light, imperishable food fit to sustain a man and woman – one injured and the other sick – who must undertake a long, demanding journey.

Revitalized by the living ambience of the great herd, Lavery came to help her. She glanced up at him and her face was radiant. She cut off a piece of brisket and held it out to him, grinning delightedly when he took it and tore off a piece with his teeth. It was his idea to make a stove out of two empty oil cans upon which the fat which Konala had gathered could be rendered into white cakes that would provide food *and* fuel in the times ahead.

Several days of brisk, clear weather followed. While the meat dried on the bushes, Konala laboured on, cutting and stitching clothing for them both. She worked herself so hard that her cheeks again showed the flame of fever and her rasping cough grew worse. When Lavery tried to make her take things a little easier she became impatient with him. Konala knew what she knew.

Finally on a day in mid-September she decided they were ready. With Lavery limping at her side, she turned her back on the white men's fine machine and set out to find her people.

The skies darkened and cold gales began sweeping gusts of snow across the bogs whose surfaces were already crusting with ice crystals. One day a sleet storm forced them into early camp. Konala had left the little travel tent to gather willows for the fire and Lavery was dozing when he heard her cry of warning through the shrilling of the wind.

There was no mistaking the urgency in her voice. Snatching up the spear he limped from the tent to see Konala running across a narrow valley. Behind her, looming immense and forbidding in the leaden light, was one of the great brown bears of the barrenlands.

Seeing Lavery poised on the slope above her, Konala swerved away, even though this brought her closer to the bear. It took a moment for Lavery to realize that she was attempting to distract the beast, then he raised the spear and flung himself down the slope, shouting and cursing at the top of his lungs.

The bear's interest in the woman shifted to the surprising spectacle Lavery presented. It sat up on its massive haunches and peered doubtfully at him through the veil of sleet.

When he was a scant few yards from the bear, Lavery tripped and fell, rolling helplessly among the rocks to fetch up on his back staring upward into that huge, square face. The bear looked back impassively then snorted, dropped on all fours and shambled off.

The meeting with the bear crystallized the changes which had been taking place in Lavery. Clad in caribou-skin clothing, a dark beard ringing his cheeks, and his hair hanging free to his shoulders, he had acquired a look of litheness and vigour – and of watchfulness. No longer was he an alien in an inimical land. He was a man now in his own right, able to make his way in an elder world.

In Konala's company he knew a unity that he had previously felt only with members of his bombing crew. The weeks they had spent together had eroded the barrier of language and he was beginning to understand much about her that had earlier baffled him. Yet the core of the enigma remained for he had not found the answer to the question that had haunted him since she brought life back to his body on that distant southern ridge.

For some time they had been descending an already frozen and snow-covered river which Konala had given him to understand would lead them to the coast. But with each passing day, Konala had been growing weaker even as Lavery regained his strength. At night, when she supposed him to be asleep, she sometimes moaned softly, and during the day she could walk only for short distances between paroxysms of coughing that left blood stains in the new snow at her feet.

When the first real blizzard struck them, it was Lavery who set up the travel tent and lit the fire of lichens and caribou fat upon which to simmer some dried deer meat. Konala lay under their sleeping robes while he prepared the meal, and when he turned to her he saw how the lines of pain around her mouth had deepened into crevices. He came close and held a tin of warm soup to her dry lips. She drank a mouthful then lay back, her dark eyes glittering too brightly in the meagre firelight. He looked deep into them and read the confirmation of his fear.

Keeping her eyes on his, she took a new pair of skin boots from under the robes and slowly stroked them, feeling the infinitely fine stitching which would keep them waterproof. After a time she reached out and placed them in his lap. Then she spoke, slowly and carefully so he would be sure to understand.

"They are not very good boots but they might carry you to the camps of my people. They might help you return to your land.... Walk well in them ... my brother."

Later that night the gale rose to a crescendo. The cold drove into the tent and, ignoring the faint flicker of the fire, pierced through the thick caribou robes wrapped about Konala and entered into her.

When the storm had blown itself out, Lavery buried her under a cairn of rocks on the high banks of the nameless river. As he made his way northward in the days that followed, his feet finding their own sure way, he no longer pondered the question which had lain in his mind through so many weeks... for he could still hear the answer she had made and would forever hear it: Walk well ... my brother....

Frank Rasky is a Canadian journalist whose work includes scripts written for dramatic films produced by the NFB and radio and television documentaries produced by the CBC. A former staff writer for *The Vancouver Sun, The New York Herald Tribune,* and the *Toronto Star,* he has more recently devoted himself to popularizing Canadian history. In *Great Canadian Disasters* (1961), *The Taming of the Canadian West* (1967), *The Polar Voyagers* (1976), and its sequel *The North Pole or Bust* (1977), his object has been "to breathe life into the bare bones of…complex personalities" while basing his work on documented fact.

The search for the Northwest Passage is one of the most persistent themes of Canadian history from the seventeenth to the twentieth century. The early voyagers were lured by images of the Grand Khan's palaces roofed with gold, of Japanese potentates dressed in silks and adorned with gems, and of the Spice Islands where one might acquire nutmeg, cloves, cinnamon, spikenard, and pepper. In the nineteenth century the whole Arctic coast of Canada was charted as a result of the search for Sir John Franklin, who disappeared with all his men in 1845. Though the English dominated polar exploration, it was a Norwegian, Roald Amundsen, who finally navigated the passage from the Atlantic to the Pacific in 1906. Many of those who failed to achieve their objective have gained, nevertheless, a kind of immortality, for their names are commemorated on the map of the North: Frobisher, Baffin, James, Foxe, Davis, Bylot, Kane, McClintock, Franklin, Ross, Peary, Gilbert, Barents, Smith, and Mackenzie.

In considering the motivations of the Arctic explorers Rasky has concluded:

Indeed, some were driven by a hunger for glory or for wealth. Some were driven by an almost masochistic need to test their strength and cunning against a hostile environment, as though stricken with a death wish. Some were driven by the scientist's, the collector's, the sportsman's instinct. And some were driven by the simple trailblazer's desire to be the first to break into new country.

One of the best remembered geographically is Henry Hudson whose name was given to a large river in New York state, a strait between northern Quebec and Baffin Island, and a great bay, not to mention an important trading company. His story was first told by his contemporary, Samuel Purchas, in *Purchas, His Pilgrimes, Contayning a History of the World in Sea Voyages and Lande Travells, by Englishmen and Others* (1625).

Mutiny on Hudson Bay

Frank Rasky

It is perhaps the best-known picture ever painted about the aftermath of a mutiny, and despite its sentimentality, the pathos of the scene is still powerful enough to break your heart. There is Henry Hudson, the noble old man with the long gray beard, cast adrift amid the ice floes in a small boat with his young son, Jack, and seven scurvy-sick men. They are left abandoned without food, without water, without clothing to protect them against the chill void of Hudson Bay.

The time is 1611, but the subjects seem frozen in a timeless limbo. The explorer sits at the tiller in his "motley" gown, vainly trying to steer the shallop through the bluish white maze of icebergs that loom around him like spectral wraiths. Cowering at his feet, thinly clad like a court page boy, lies Jack, his fingers reaching out for the warmth of his father's hand. Huddled beside them is the loyal crew member, Philip Staffe, the ship's carpenter who told the mutineers he would not be party to their villainy and instead chose "for the love of the Master to go down to the shallop".

What makes the picture so piteous is the look in Hudson's eyes. They are the eyes of a beaten man, totally dejected, staring into space with utter hopelessness.

It is an affecting scene, perhaps true in the sense that the artist has captured the mood of the melodrama, and yet it is a false one. The picture, which hangs in the Tate Gallery of London, is purely imaginative. The artist, the Honorable John Collier, painted it in the Victorian era some three hundred years after the event. It is a distortion, not only because no likeness of Henry Hudson is known to exist; but because it presents a one-dimensional portrait of the explorer's complex character.

One would like to remember Hudson as a paragon of virtue, the guiltless innocent done in by crafty villains. This is the black-and-white image which the painter and the historians of the Victorian age preferred to idealize. But a study of the facts today casts Hudson in a less noble light. He remains a sympathetic figure, but blemished with failings that make him appear more human to us.

His contemporary, William Shakespeare, who probed into the grays of the human heart so profoundly, portrayed a strikingly similar flawed hero in his *Tragedy of King Lear*. Like that doomed old man, also driven to the point of insanity by his own follies, Hudson was both imperious and capricious; exasperatingly moody and indecisive; given to crankiness intermixed with gentle forgiveness; a player of favorites; a poor judge of people; betrayed by the very favorites whose gratitude he so injudiciously sought.

His ultimate weakness was that he was a too-accommodating leader of men, vacillating when he should have been firm, placating when he should have been tough. In one of the few fragments of his personal journals that have been preserved, he remarks that the stormy seas, thanks to God, were "assuaged". He might have been speaking of his own philosophy; he was too intent on assuaging his mutinous crews, and in the end, they destroyed him.

And yet those journals also reveal that he could be considerate and kind, very determined and very brave in surmounting unflinchingly the calamities that Shakespeare called "sea sorrows". He seemed possessed by the intellectual curiosity of the impassioned discoverer, who does not necessarily want to reach a goal, but who is driven on and on, risking his life to see what fresh wonders he might find on the other side of the next iceberg. Perhaps he might discover – as he thought he did – a mermaid in the sea, or tropical heat near the Pole. He was the single-minded optimist, credulous with hope. No matter what the personal consequences, he was bent on solving geographical puzzles, or else, as he phrased it, "to give reason wherefore it will not be"....

84   Frank Rasky

On April 17, 1610, with the backing of a syndicate of wealthy English merchants headed by Sir Dudley Digges and Sir John Wolstenholme, Henry Hudson sailed the fifty-five-ton *Discovery* down the river Thames on his last ill-starred voyage of discovery.

Only eight of the twenty-three discoverers aboard were fated to see England again. They were an oddly assorted ragtag-and-bobtail of a crew. Perhaps none was more odd than the scribe who saved his neck from the gallows by leaving to posterity a highly biased record of the tragic events. He bore the improbable name of Abacuk Prickett. A one-time haberdasher, he had become a manservant to the expedition's patron, Sir Dudley Digges, and his master had sent along the valet to keep an eye on his investment. Prickett was a servile, Uriah Heepish sort of puritan, who covered up his suspect behaviour with treacly quotations from Holy Writ. His unctuous hypocrisy reminds one of King Lear's revelation: "See how yond justice rails upon yond simple thief....change places, and, handy-dandy, which is the justice, which is the thief?"

Prickett railed largely at another odd passenger aboard the Ship of Fools. This was Henry Greene, who in company with first mate Robert Juet, was to become a ringleader of the final infamous mutiny. Again Shakespeare, in his *Tragedy of King Lear,* summed up Henry Greene in a phrase: "The prince of darkness is a gentleman." Greene was a clever, well-educated young gentleman from a respectable family in Kent. He was gifted at writing, a bit of a snob, something of a dueller, and evidently an atheist. He shocked the Scripture-quoting Prickett with his assertion that when it came to religion he was a clean sheet of paper whereon Prickett could write as he pleased. Greene also seems to have been a hell-raising wastrel, who squandered his money on bawds in taverns. His own mother, we are told, would trust him with no more than four pounds, so he could buy a new suit appropriate to wear on the expedition. Hudson had taken a fancy to the charming ne'er-do-well, given him meat, drink, and lodgings at his London home, and had promised to find his protégé a place in Prince Henry's regiment of guards after the voyage was over.

Hudson appears to have sneaked Greene aboard ship at Gravesend, without the knowledge of the ship owners, and this show of favoritism seems to have galled other officers of the crew. Their smoldering resentment broke out soon after the *Discovery* touched Iceland. They bathed in a hot spring at Lousy Bay, where "the water was so hot it would scald a fowl," and Prickett read baneful augury in the sight of erupting Mount Hecla, "which cast out much fire, a sign of foul weather to come".

The mutinous fire on ice began blazing with a furious fight between Henry Greene and the ship's surgeon. Hudson unwisely condoned the wild behavior of his young protégé. Old Juet, sensing that the captain had rejected him for a new favorite, took out his venom in a drunken tirade. The first mate charged that Hudson's new pet had been taken on as a stool pigeon to "crack his credit" with the captain. Furthermore, Juet muttered about the crew's need to keep swords and muskets ready in their cabins for the bloody manslaughter looming ahead. Not content with that, in the hearing of his skipper, the first mate threatened to turn the head of the ship homeward from the action.

Hudson was at first enraged, for he vowed that he would leave his old shipmate beached on Lousy Bay. Then he was placating, for we are told that he eventually "pacified" Juet, "hoping of amendment".

With these seeds of jealousy and rancor planted, Hudson steered his unhappy ship toward the hellish riptides known then as the Furious Overfall and better known today as the mouth of Hudson Strait. His men were thrown into a sick funk by the spectacle, and little wonder.

The strait is a bottleneck, a hundred miles wide and four hundred and fifty miles long, boiling with currents. It is the funnel outlet of North America's biggest inland sea. This is Hudson Bay, which is six hundred and fifty miles wide and eight hundred and fifty miles long – a mammoth milk bottle containing two hundred and ninety-four thousand square miles of frozen salt water. The bay and strait are relatively ice-free and navigable no more than three months of the year, from mid-July until October. But the *Discovery* tried to enter the strait on June 25. At that time the bottleneck is an uncorked fury – a maelstrom of churning, pulverizing ice pans escaping from the bay into the open sea.

Hudson himself was dismayed by the sight of somersaulting bergs in the "great and whirling" turbulent tides. He later confessed he felt he "should never have got out of this ice but there have perished". Buffeted by floating ice islands, he tacked desperately in the strait's gateway between the sentinel cliffs on the banks of Baffin Island to the north and Labrador's Torngat Mountains to the south. With a twinge of wavering indecision, he democratically showed the crew his chart and took a vote whether they should proceed any further, yea or nay.

"Whereupon some were of one mind and some of another," we are told, "some wishing themselves at home and some not caring where, so they were out of the ice."

One crew member swore that if he had a hundred pounds, he'd give ninety pounds of it to be back in England. But Philip Staffe, the stout-hearted ship's carpenter from Ipswich, differed. "If he had a hundred, he'd not give ten pounds upon such condition, but would think it to be as good money as ever he had, and to bring it as well home."

Hudson slithered and lurched on blindly through a hammering storm and coiling mists and marblelike waters. On July 8 his resolution was strengthened as he skirted a bay on the strait's southern shores. This region of north Quebec today bears the romantic name of Ungava, Eskimo for "Far Away"; and Hudson evidently sighted its Akpatok Island, Eskimo for "Place Where Auk Birds Are Caught". It was a high, haycock land powdered with snow, but populous with ptarmigan and polar bears, and somehow it caught Hudson's imagination. He saw it as a "champagne land" and named it "Desire Provoketh", and his curiosity was provoked to search on westward. No matter if he was being drawn to his own damnation, the obsessed discoverer was prepared to damn the consequences.

On he sailed. Past wrinkled brown mountains of "riven rocks and plashes of water". Past a startled polar bear who "cast her head between her hind legs and then dived under the ice". Past rippling whirlpools and rustling cascades. Past icebergs parading by like a procession of opaline pagodas from Cipango.

At last he reached the end of the strait, and made a left turn, and triumphantly, records Hudson, "we put through the narrow passage." For it was here the *Discovery* sailed between two lofty headlands, basaltic cliffs lancing two thousand feet high, which guard entry into the burnished blue waters of Hudson Bay.

"The head of this entrance on the south side I named Cape Wolstenholme, and the head on the northwester shore I called Cape Digges," wrote Hudson on August 3, 1610. "Then I observed and found the ship at noon in 61 degrees, 20 minutes, and a sea to the westward...."

His journal there breaks off, and it is the last entry we have from his surviving fragment of a log, the remainder of which was destroyed by the mutineers. Yet one can well imagine, as a contemporary says, that Hudson felt "proudly confident that he had won" the Passage to Cathay. Surely that was the open Pacific Ocean he saw beckoning invitingly westward and southward.

Hudson was so impatient to go on that he wouldn't let his crew members delay to pick up fresh meat they had uncovered at Cape Digges. Prickett, whose dubious journal we must now rely on, had taken a boatload of mariners ashore to the cliffs of Digges Island. There they had found Eskimo stone cairns stored like a butcher shop with plentiful "fowls hanged by their necks" – possibly the long-necked, chestnut-colored birds named after the explorer's bay, Hudsonian godwits.

The valet tells us he tried to persuade Master Hudson to stay there for a couple of days. The ship was provisioned for just six months, and they could replenish their dwindling pantry by looting the Eskimo poultry larders. "But by no means would he stay." The Master recklessly ordered the crew to push on. "So we left the fowl," says Prickett with obvious resentment, "and lost our way" poking fruitlessly for three months down the east coast of Hudson Bay "in a labyrinth without end."

It must have been a frustrating disappointment for Hudson. There he was groping through the coastal mists for a glimpse of the glinting gold roofs of Japan and hoping to smell the sweet fragrance of the balm-bearing Spice Islands. Instead he cruised by the bald Pre-Cambrian rock sites of such Eskimo villages as Ivugivik, meaning "Place of the Piling up of Ice", and perhaps pushed past that loveliest-sounding of Eskimo names, Povungnituk, which bears the unlovely translation of "Place of the Stinking Caribou."

By September Hudson was growing desperate. He was boxed in a blind alley at the very bottom of Hudson Bay – the shallow cul-de-sac now known as James Bay. His officers were in a sullen, lowering mood. They taunted their skipper as he beat back and forth uncertainly, north and south, east and west, in a futile attempt to find his dreamed-of thoroughfare. And Robert Juet jeered at the Master's vain "hope to see Bantam in Java by Candlemas".

Hudson's nerves, already frayed, snapped at this sarcastic jest. He held an open mutiny trial. All the allegations of Juet's past "abuses and slanders" were raked over. It resulted in Juet being stripped of his rank and his pay. Replacing him as first mate was a mariner "who had showed himself honestly respecting the good of the action". This was Robert Bylot, an able but ambiguous pilot, a shadowy mixture of fidelity and treason. While he was about it, Hudson also demoted the boatswain and elevated to that position a rough, brawny hooligan named William Wilson.

With characteristic capriciousness, Hudson assuaged the former favorites he had just deposed. "If the offenders yet behaved themselves henceforth honestly", he promised them, he "would be a means for their good and forget injuries".

But sulking Robert Juet could neither forget nor forgive being ridiculed like a castoff lover, and we are told he "nursed his hatred like a red-eyed ferret in the hutch of his dark soul".

According to Prickett, Hudson's temper and irritability soon grew strained to the point of irrationality. By November 1 the *Discovery* was beset by ice beside the dun-colored rocks and tidal mudflats at the mouth of the Rupert River. And by November 10 they were frozen in for the winter. They found themselves, at about 51 degrees north latitude, beached in the subarctic bleakness in the southeast pocket of James Bay.

Even today it seems a haunted place. The silence of the bay is pierced by the plaintive cry of the red-throated loons, as though they are protesting their fate. And strewn all around the frost-shattered ground are granite ridges, looking like upended tombstones. It is just south of the tree line, where stunted black spruce and jackpine verge into tundra. The trees are tilted, leaning now one way, now another, like a drunken dwarf forest, their branches bald on the north side, because their leaves have been shorn clean by the cutting winds.

They spent a dreadful winter there, racked by cold and scurvy and fractious querulousness. Hudson first alienated his sole officer who appears to have been genuinely loyal to him, Philip Staffe. After a seemingly senseless long delay, Hudson ordered the ship's carpenter to cut down trees and build a house ashore.

"The carpenter told him that the snow and frost were such as he neither could nor would go in hand with such work," says Prickett. "Which when our Master heard, he ferreted him out of the cabin to strike him, calling him by many foul names and threatening to hang him. The carpenter told him that he knew what belonged to his place better than himself, and that he was no house carpenter. So this passed, and the house was after made with much labour, but to no end."

Hudson next made the more crucial mistake of picking a quarrel with that hell-raising gentleman, Henry Greene. The ship's gunner having died of scurvy, Hudson had promised to let Greene have the dead man's gaberdine cloak. But Greene, apparently out of sheer mischief, went out hunting for ptarmigan with the Ipswich carpenter who had just fallen out of favor with Hudson. On their return, Hudson was so peeved that he retaliated by bestowing the gaberdine gown instead upon his current favorite, Robert Bylot, newly elevated to first mate,

Greene immediately challenged Hudson for breaking his promise. We are told that Hudson exploded into a fury and reviled his one-time protégé with words of disgrace. Hudson told the profligate that "all his friends would not trust him with twenty shillings, and therefore why should he? As for wages, he had none, nor none should have, if he did not please him well."

With malevolence, Henry Greene joined the estranged Robert Juet in whispering words of revenge against their erratic Master. And there must have been a touch of madness there, in the frosty air at the edge of the bay, for soon Hudson was playing his reckless game of favorites again. He demoted first mate Robert Bylot and enthroned instead an ignoramus named John King.

"To speak of all the troubles of this cold winter," says Prickett, "would be tedious." It was a kind of hornet's nest on ice, so freezing that Prickett was crippled lame and another seaman had the nails frozen off his toes. "Herod's daughter", the mariners' nickname for scurvy, broke out. Until conifer buds dispelled the sickness, their gums blackened and the jawbones rotted around their teeth. Sheer hunger drove them into eating frogs and moss, "than which", says Prickett, with the distaste of a gentleman's gentleman accustomed to serving Sir Dudley Digges malmsey wine and English roast beef, "I take the powder of a post to be much better".

Their hopes rose in spring with the coming of a few migratory birds and the first Indian or Eskimo they'd seen. Hudson gave the shy native a knife, mirror, and buttons. With enticing signs the captain promised the visitor more if he would return with provisions.

The native came back the next day pulling a sled heaped with two beaver skins and two deer skins. He returned the gifts which Hudson had given him and proceeded to barter. Sad to say, white man's greed – the same greed which later induced the Hudson's Bay Company to set up the Rupert's House trading post at almost that very spot – bedeviled Henry Hudson, its first overly avaricious fur trader.

"The Master showed him a hatchet, for which he would have given the Master one of his deer skins," says Prickett of Hudson's hard bargaining. "But our Master would have them both; and so he had, although not willingly. After many signs of his people to the north and to the south, and that after so many sleeps he would come again, he went his way, but never came back any more."

Having thus scared off a potential food provider, Hudson ventured out in the shallop alone in a last desperate attempt to acquire meat from the other native tribesmen. He came back nine days later reporting failure. The natives had actually set fire to the woods when they saw him coming.

He returned to find his crew in literal terror of starvation. Their fishing netted them no more than fourscore small trout, "a poor relief for so many hungry bellies". And apparently they had provisions left for only two more weeks. We are told that Hudson distributed to his men their remaining rations of a pound of bread each and divided five cheeses among them.

"And he wept when he gave it to them."

His men were not moved by his tears. If Prickett's testimony is to be believed, Hudson was not entirely blameless for the ensuing outburst of anarchy and pent-up grievances. For by mid-June, when he had the *Discovery* in the open water of James Bay, the explorer seems to have cracked up emotionally. The stresses of privation and the trials of taming a recalcitrant crew came close to unhinging his mind.

First he had the cabin boy break open the sea chests of the crew to search for hidden bread. It was said that the boy delivered to the Master thirty loaves in a bag. This was a foolhardy risk to take with men like Juet, who had already murdered purloining Indians for rummaging through his personal belongings.

Secondly it was claimed that Hudson himself had been hoarding reserves of provisions. The mutineers unanimously charged in Admiralty Court later that the captain had cut a secret scuttle from the hold to his cabin, and there he had stored his private supply: two hundred ship's biscuits, a peck of meal, cheeses, a keg of beer, and aqua vitae brandy. Allegedly he summoned his favorites to his cabin and doled out food and drink to keep up the strength of the privileged few. If true, this was inexcusable, for a shipmaster to play God with his men and choose who was to starve and who was to live.

But finally, to cite Shakespeare, it was something "more fell than anguish, hunger, or the sea" that stirred the simmering malcontents into open rebellion. After a winter's soliloquy, Hudson's insatiable curiosity was not yet stilled, and it was this mania that his puzzled men could neither understand nor tolerate. The dreamer was apparently determined to continue searching for the Northwest Passage, even if it meant leaving some of his men behind. The Reverend Samuel Purchas, his sympathetic geography tutor, who had all the evidence before him, unwittingly drops a damning phrase in his summary of the tragedy. The parson tells us that a few days after Hudson had his ship becalmed in a James Bay ice field, "their victuals being almost spent, and he, out of his despair, *letting fall some words of setting some on shore,* the conspirators…entered his cabin in the night." The italics are not his, but the chilling significance of what he revealed has been overlooked by Hudson's apologists.

And yet, for all his failings, Hudson might well have exclaimed with King Lear, "I am a man more sinn'd against than sinning!" For the explorer suffered the ultimate anguish of being forsaken by the very ingrates upon whom he had lavished the greatest kindness.

There were three Judases who were the principal ringleaders of the mutiny. There was Henry Greene, the scapegrace daredevil of the conspiracy, who said he "would rather be hanged at home than starved abroad". There was Robert Juet, sly in his deviousness and brooding with vindictiveness, who "swore plainly he would justify this deed when he came home". And there was the muscle of the revolt, William Wilson, who would fain be a pirate rather than an elevated boatswain, and who was tigerish to get on with the bloody action "while it was hot".

On Saturday night, June 21, 1611, the unholy trio crept stealthily into Abacuk Prickett's cabin and the cabal made the lackey privy to their plot. They intended to cast the Master, his favorites, and the feeblest members of the crew into the shallop and let them shift for themselves.

"For there they lay," said the intriguers, "the Master not caring to go one way or other; and they had not eaten anything these three days; and therefore were resolute either to mend or end; and what they had begun, they would go through with it or die."

Prickett claims he tried to dissuade them. They were married men, with wives and children, and for the sake of their loved ones how could they commit so vile a crime in the sight of God? He would not sanction any mischief that reeked of blood and revenge. Eventually he managed to salve his conscience; for he joined four other conspirators in swearing an oath on the Bible that their scheme was designed for the "good of the action, with no harm to no man". It was a sanctimonious pretext; for Prickett tells us in the next breath that a prime mover of the oath-taking was the atheistic Henry Greene, who flew into a rage swearing to "cut his throat", of any man who might impede their nefarious plan.

"If there be no remedy," Prickett consoled himself piously, "the will of God be done."

Prickett urged them to wait for three days or two days before they perpetrated the deed. But William Wilson would not wait, and jested sardonically to Henry Greene about the valet's qualms, "He is in his old song, still patient."

Prickett seems to have swallowed his qualms at least partially. "I hoped," we hear him muttering, "that some one or other would give some notice...to the Master." Yet the valet, with elastic morality, did not think to risk his own skin by giving that warning to the Master. So it is manifest that Prickett thus became a silent accessory to the crime. Reviewing the evil doings later, Prickett's contemporary, Captain Luke Foxe, who was also to explore Hudson Bay, made the incisive indictment: "Well, *Prickett,* I am in great doubt of thy fidelity to Master *Hudson!*"

In his journal Prickett sets the scene for the skulduggery as though it were a melodrama out of the Old Testament. "It was dark," he writes, "and they in a readiness to put this deed of darkness in execution. I called to Henry Greene and Wilson, and prayed them not to go in hand with it in the dark, but to stay till morning. Now, every man, I hoped, would go to his rest. But wickedness sleepeth not. For Henry Greene keepeth the Master company all night and others are as watchful as he."

When dawn broke over the shimmering ice field on Sunday morning, Henry Hudson stepped out of his cabin. Waiting for him were William Wilson and two confederates. The thugs pounced on the captain and pinioned his arms behind him with rope.

"What did they mean?" asked Hudson.

"He should know what they meant," said Wilson, "when he was cast in the shallop."

While Hudson was struggling with his captors, Robert Juet went below to settle a grudge. He wanted to seize personally Hudson's current favorite, who had superseded both himself and Robert Bylot as first mate. This was the former quartermaster, John King, who could neither write nor read, and it galled Juet that yet "the Master loved him and made him his mate." John King put up a fight for his life. He drew out his sword and almost killed Juet; but other conspirators overpowered him and hurled him down into the shallop.

One by one the other victims, "the poor, the sick, the lame men", were pulled out of their cabins and dragged along the deck and heaved into the small sailing boat that was tied to the ship's stern. "To most of them," the testimony was later read in British Admiralty Court, "it was utterly unknown who should go, or who tarry, but as affection or rage did guide them in that fury that were authors and executors of that plot."

One crew member, Thomas Woodhouse, described as a student of mathematics, was thrust out of the ship into the shallop weeping. He vainly implored the executioners to take his keys and share his goods if only they would let him stay aboard.

Two treacherous seamen, Arnold Lodlo and Michael Butt, were themselves implicated in double treachery. Both were fellow mutineers who mocked at Hudson's favorites, John King and the captain's cabin-boy son, Jack, for their knavery. In a sudden reversal of whims, Henry Greene decided to jettison his two henchmen, and "with much ado" the pair of knaves were dumped kicking and screaming beside the victims they had just tormented.

Out of that horror emerged one hero with honor. Philip Staffe, the Ipswich carpenter, had once been threatened with a flogging by the Master for balking at building a house on a snowbank. But when it came to murder on ice, he had a conscience and loyalty that told him where a Christian's duty stood.

The mutineers entreated him to stay. They had need of his strength and his skills.

"Let them be hanged," he said. He would not stay in the ship unless they forced him. Out of love for the Master, he chose "rather to commit himself to God's mercy in the forlorn shallop than with such villains to accept of likelier hopes".

They bade him go then, for they would not stay him.

"I will," said he, "so I may have my chest with me, and all that is in it."

Silently the traitors passed down to the good carpenter from Ipswich his chest of tools, and in recognition of an honest man, gave him as well a fowling piece, a little meal, and an iron pot.

His wrists bound behind his back, clad only in a motley morning gown, Hudson went down to his doom with a final stunned awareness of betrayal by those whom he had once befriended. It was later charged in British Admiralty Court that the ringleaders had auctioned off before the mast the very clothes of their captain; and although he denied it, Robert Bylot, the suspiciously noncommital criminal accomplice, was accused of stealing Hudson's finger ring.

As the mutineers led the captain down the hatch, says Prickett, "The Master called to me. I came out of my cabin as well as I could to the hatchway to speak to him. There on my knees I besought them for the love of God to remember themselves, and to do as they would be done unto. They bade me keep myself well, and get me into my cabin, not suffering the Master to speak with me."

The lamed Prickett then crawled over to his cabin window, and as they flung Hudson into the shallop, he heard the Master shout at him, "It is that villain, Juet, that hath undone us!"

"Nay," cried out Prickett, "it is that villain, Henry Greene," and Prickett adds, "and I spake it not softly."

The mutineers quickly got the ship under way, towed the little shallop until they neared the edge of the ice, and then cut it adrift. And so they sailed northward, leaving behind their shipmates, the Master and his son and seven men, marooned "without food, drink, fire, clothing, or any necessaries, maliciously abandoned to their death".

Now that the deed was done, in the phrase of one of Hudson's biographers, Llewelyn Powys, a "paroxysm of licence" gripped the mutineers. Within a half hour they ransacked every inch of the *Discovery* like robbers who have slain the good man of the house. They grabbed at clothes in the lockers, looted belongings in sea chests, wrangled over whether Robert Juet or Robert Bylot was to serve as chief pilot and, of course, they gobbled up the food and liquor secreted in the captain's cabin as well as the remaining provisions discovered in the hold – a vessel of meal, two firkins of butter, a half bushel of peas, twenty-seven pieces of brined pork.

While they fought over the spoils, a blood-chilling cry arose. The shallop was in sight, and like some skeletal nemesis, was following them.

Whereupon, Prickett tells us, "they let fall the mainsail, and out with their topsail, and fly as from an enemy."

One can only surmise how Hudson must have felt, a forsaken figure in his gown of many colors, standing and staring as his last hope of survival vanished amid the blue mists and white ice fields of his vast uncharted bay. Perhaps like mad Lear, cast away on the blasted heath with his fool, he may have cried out to the heavens to inflict justice on his persecutors:

A plague upon you, murderers, traitors all!

And indeed terrible retribution struck down the guiltiest of the betrayers. The thirteen aboard the *Discovery* spent five weeks fumbling blindly, like frightened children in the dark, in the direction of Hudson Strait. They were smitten by "stout gales of wind" and ripping rocks and clutching ice "into the which we ran from thin to thick, till we could go no further for ice."

And all the while they quarelled among themselves for their depleted rations of food. Prickett tells us that the godless Henry Greene, who had assumed the role of Master, gradually became satanic in his hunger. "He began (very subtly) to draw me to take upon me to search for those things which he himself had stolen. And he accused me of a matter no less than treason amongst us: that I had deceived the company of thirty cakes of bread."

With his fund of phrases from scripture, one wonders why the glibly pietistic valet saw no parallel with the thirty pieces of silver.

At length, towards the end of July, they sighted the sea fowl screaming and wheeling over the lancing cliffs of Digges Island, and there a kind of poetic justice caught up with some of them. Prickett went ashore with a boatload of mutineers to do some trading with a band of Eskimos. The kayakers welcomed them with friendly dancing and leaping, showed them how to snare birds, and offered the Englishmen walrus tusks for barter. But Henry Greene, brandishing such knick-knacks as mirrors, jew's harps, and bells, seems to have alienated the native traders; for "he swore they should have nothing till he had venison."

The upshot was a savage Eskimo onslaught. Henry Greene, yelling "Coragio!", laid about him with his truncheon, says Prickett; but the duellist was slain outright by a shower of arrows. Prickett himself, after grappling a knife away from an Eskimo, ("God enabling me"), slit his assailant's throat with a Scottish dirk; but God, alas, didn't enable the valet to escape until "I received a cruel wound in my back." William Wilson had his "bowels cut"; and that tigerish boatswain, who had been so hot for bloody action, died bloodily "swearing and cursing in most fearful manner". Altogether four mutineers were slain gruesomely, and their shipmates had so little regard for their one-time ringleader, Henry Greene, that they dumped that gentleman atheist's corpse from the row-boat into the sea without burial rites.

Robert Juet suffered the slower and more agonizing death of scurvy and starvation. After they had eaten the sea fowl they had caught at Digges Island, the mutineers expiated their sins on a famishing diet of seaweed fried in candle grease, and feathers and bones consumed with vinegar. Five weeks later, when the *Discovery* rolled and bucketed into an Irish seaport, its untended sails flapping aimlessly in the wind like a scarecrow, only one man, Robert Bylot, had strength enough to lie upon the helm to steer. The other seven scurvy-sick survivors were strewn about the deck like bony ghouls. And Robert Juet, after a futile attempt to escape the gallows by directing the ship to Newfoundland, had finally "died of mere want". As Parson Samuel Purchas sermonized in summary, "Everywhere can Divine Justice find executioners."

Yet in the end mercantile cupidity was stronger than divine justice. The Masters of Trinity House examined the eight surviving mutineers and judged "they all deserve to be hanged." But the High Court of the Admiralty, evidently with an avaricious eye on the potential British commerce that the parasites might produce, waited an unseemly seven years and then declared them guiltless of murder or treason. Indeed, the merchants were so greedy for gain that Robert Bylot and Abacuk Prickett were hired almost immediately to steer the *Discovery* on an unsuccessful expedition, in 1612, to exploit the Northwest Passage to the Indies supposedly lying beyond "Hudson, his Bay". And the evidence suggests that Bylot, as pilot, made no attempt whatsoever to search for Master Hudson at the bottom of his bay.

The moral of the Hudson story, if there is any, was probably best suggested by Shakespeare. The dramatist tells us of the mariner who watched the sharks destroy their prey and asked, "Master, I marvel how the fishes live in the sea?" And his Master answered, "Why, as men do aland; the great ones eat up the little ones."

The fate of Henry Hudson, his son Jack, and the seven castaway seamen remains a mystery to this day. At their British Admiralty trial, the mutineers testified that the *Discovery* had eventually "lost sight of them and never heard of them since". Explorer Thomas James, after whom the very bottom of the bay is named, himself spent a dreadful winter there twenty years after the mutiny; he said he found wooden stakes driven into the ground which may have been sharpened by the iron tools of Hudson's carpenter. The evidence is not conclusive, but it may be so.

All one can do is cite Shakespeare again, and conclude that the heroic yet tragically flawed figure wrought his own ruin; and that the dreamer almost wilfully chose as his destiny to:

Lie where the light foam of the sea may beat
Thy gravestone daily.

And so consumed by curiosity and beset by his ego-driven sea sorrows, Henry Hudson, like other obsessed explorers who followed in his footsteps, lost his life discovering that the illusory Polar Passage was, after all, "but a Point, but Nothing, but Vanitie".

William D. Blankenship was born in Chicago and was educated at the University of Southern California School of Journalism. He now lives in Ridgefield, Connecticut, and works for IBM as a writer and editor. In addition to *Yukon Gold* (1977), from which the following story is taken, he has written *The Helix File, The Programmed Men,* and *Tiger Ten.*

Yukon Gold is the kind of high-spirited adventure story that might strike one as being a tall tale, with its beautiful and clever heroine, its errant but lovable Mountie, its avalanches, murders, steamboat hi-jacking, and a collection of confidence men, thugs, gamblers, and thieves that seems to have stepped out of a Damon Runyon yarn. But the Soapy Smith gang really did terrorize Skagway and the Yukon; Colonel Sam Steele and his North-West Mounted Police really did mount guard on the summit of White Pass to hold the criminals at bay, while Inspector Constantine attempted to maintain the law in the Yukon; and for a brief year from July 1898, to July 1899, Dawson City was "the San Francisco of the North". According to Pierre Berton's *Klondike,* it had a telephone service, running water, steam heat, electricity, dozens of hotels, motion picture and vaudeville theatres, dramatic societies, church choirs, and restaurants "where string orchestras played 'Cavalleria Rusticana' for men in tailcoats who ate paté de foie gras and drank vintage wines".

Blankenship follows in the tradition of Jack London and Robert Service, who attributed to the Yukon of gold rush days a romantic aura that it has never lost. For the hundreds of prospectors who struck it rich, and even more, perhaps, for the thousands who did not, the gold rush was the high point of their lives. A desire to recapture that magical atmosphere – and not only for commercial reasons – has spawned such modern entertainments as Edmonton's Klondike Days and Dawson City's summer festival.

100

Trial in the Bank Saloon
William D. Blankenship

On the evening of January 15, 1898, I witnessed the killing of Mike Lynch, a bartender at the Bank Saloon and Gambling House in Dawson, Yukon Territory. It was the first murder of the year in Dawson, and greeted as a welcome event.

There was nothing I could do to stop the crime. I could only arrest the killer, a handyman and occasional gold prospector named Rollo Moon. I was occupying my customary place at the Bank's bar when, out of the corner of my eye, I saw Rollo draw a knife. I managed to shout "Watch yourself, Mike!" but my warning came too late. Rollo reached across the bar and drove the knife deep into Mike's chest. Mike reeled backwards, toppling a pyramid of shot glasses, and fell to the floor. He was dead when I reached him.

Mike's parka was hanging on a peg behind the bar. I covered his body with it, then arrested Rollo. He put up no struggle and I marched him outside and down Front Street toward the police barracks without even drawing my revolver.

My name is Brian Bonner and in 1898, the year of the great Gold Rush, I was one of a handful of North-West Mounted Police who kept the peace over two hundred thousand square miles of Canada's Yukon Territory. The town of Dawson was at the center of the rush, an isolated community located on the junction of the Yukon and Klondike Rivers six hundred miles from the nearest civilization and populated by gold prospectors, gamblers, traders, adventuring women, and assorted cutthroats.

In those days I was famous in the Yukon as The Man Who Killed Almighty Voice (having dispatched a notorious Cree renegade by that unlikely name) and many folks considered me the finest lawman in Canada. Like other men of large reputation, I also had my detractors. They whispered that I was a thief…drunkard…backshooter…and liar of grand scale. Unfortunately, that opinion of me has gained wide acceptance over the years.

At any rate, I locked Rollo Moon in Dawson's small jail and the following morning the place and date for his trial were set. It came as a surprise to the residents of Dawson when Inspector Constantine agreed to hold the trial in the Bank Saloon. True, the Bank qualified as *the scene of the crime*. But in the past Inspector Constantine had denied many other requests to add a flash of pageantry to his courtroom. Usually he convened his court in a tiny room at the police barracks that would hold no more than twenty people.

By contrast Silent Sam Bonnifield's Bank Saloon would hold up to three hundred people, tightly packed. Sam immediately began selling tickets to the trial at fifty dollars apiece. He raised the ticket price to one hundred dollars when it became known that Hannah Young had agreed to act as Rollo's defense counsel. The price was still a bargain. Everyone said so.

On the morning of the trial I arrived at the Bank half an hour early to find it swollen with ticket holders. I pushed my way through the crowd, reaching the bar with some difficulty, and waved for my glass and bottle. It was the management's policy to set a fresh bottle of Perry Davis Painkiller in front of me whenever I visited the Bank and to tear up my bartab when I left. In those days there wasn't a saloonkeeper in Canada who would take money from The Man Who Killed Almighty Voice. But for the first time in several years a bottle did not magically appear in front of me.

"Sorry," the bartender apologized. "No liquor for you 'till after the trial."

The man was new, Mike Lynch's replacement. I decided to show tolerance. "Look here, I'm Bonner. Constable Brian Bonner." Nice low voice, no fuss.

The bartender shifted uncomfortably. My temper is well known. On top of that I am a big handsome man who looks even bigger in a bulky elkskin parka with the brass buttons of the North-West Mounted Police down the front. I was also wearing a pistol strapped to my waist over the parka and I suppose I was in one of my belligerent moods, which probably explains why the bartender hurried through his explanation. "Constantine passed the word about you, Bonner. Like I said, no liquor 'till after the trial."

"You mean he corked the bottle on me?"

Sam Bonnifield appeared at my side. "Come on, Brian. It's not our idea. Constantine says he'll shut down the Bank for three days if you aren't sober when you testify."

"By God, Sam, that's too much! They can't treat me like a damned kid. I don't care whether I testify or not. I might not even be *called* to testify. To hell with Constantine! I'll do my drinking at the Aurora."

"The whole town is corked up. No one will pour you a drink against Constantine's orders."

People nearby were chuckling, but when I wheeled around they turned their heads or hid their grins behind glasses. "What are you *cheechakos* staring at!"

"Nothing, Brian," said Three-Inch White, who stood closest to me. "Not a thing." He moved down the bar.

"Relax," Sam coaxed in his warmest tones. "The trial starts in thirty minutes and it'll be over and done with in another quarter hour. Rollo is guilty as hell. We all saw him kill Mike Lynch. When the trial's over I'll break out my best stuff." He leaned forward, his mustache brushing my ear. "I've got a bottle of Napoleon brandy put away," he whispered. "I was saving it for spring, the day the damned ice cracks on the river. But you and me'll sample it this morning. What do you say?"

Only under very heavy pressure would Silent Sam make such a generous offer. I glanced around and began to feel that same pressure myself. The Bank was packed with Dawson's most important citizens. There was Thomas Fawcett, the Yukon gold commissioner, sharing a table with Swiftwater Bill Gates. Lord Avonmore, who had rafted downriver just before the ice jammed in September with a retinue of servants and chefs, a bulldog, a cargo of tinned hams, a lawn tennis set, and seventy cases of champagne that froze and went to vinegar, sat at the adjoining table in regal isolation. Antone Stander, one of the first Yukon prospectors to strike a million-dollar claim, shared his table with One-Eyed Riley, the Alaska Commercial Company's warehouse night watchman. And across the room sat Charles Berry, the six-foot eight-inch fruit grower from California who had pulled his bride over White Pass and down the Yukon valley by sled to stake his rich claim on Bonanza Creek. Dawson's most celebrated ladies were also present. Sitting together in their gaudiest silk dresses were Nellie the Pig, Gussie Lamore, Diamond Tooth Gertie, and half a dozen of their "sisters". William Ogilvie, the government surveyor who measured and certified the claims in the Klondike Gold District, was arguing about the depth of hardpan on Eldorado Creek with Deephole Johnson.

The loudness of my own voice made me suddenly self-conscious. They were all watching, anxious to see my full reaction to Constantine's order. If I tossed a chair through the mirror behind Sam's bar and stalked out of the Bank in a rage, that would be an added fillip to the morning's events.

So I swallowed hard and fought to bring my anger under control. "Okay, Sam. I'll have a shot of that brandy later." And I went to a chair that Swiftwater Bill had saved for me, aware of the mutterings of disappointment around me.

"Morning, Brian," Swiftwater Bill hailed. "Grab that chair before someone steals the damned thing."

Commissioner Fawcett nodded in his ponderous manner. "Hello there, Brian. You're the arresting officer, I understand. Tell me, is there any chance Rollo Moon will be acquitted?"

I shook my head. "I don't see how. Thirty people watched him kill Mike Lynch. Happened in two seconds, but we all saw it. It was a damned neat job of murder, speaking from a purely professional point of view."

"I shouldn't have done my gambling at the Aurora on Wednesday night," Bill groused. "Missed all the excitement." He winked at us. "They had a new gal at the Aurora, came upriver from Circle City by dogsled. I heard she was mighty fine lookin' but it turned out she could've been one of the sled dogs herself." Bill's expression became more serious. "I hope Constantine hangs Rollo high. Mike Lynch was the best bartender in the Yukon."

Swiftwater Bill had become one of my closest friends among the Yukon prospectors. A little string bean of a man, Bill had worked his way north two years before as a cook on a tramp steamer. After jumping ship in Nome, Bill found another cook's job on one of the stern-wheeled river-boats that plied the Yukon River between the Bering Sea and Dawson when the river was navigable. He had struck it rich on Bonanza Creek and now he wore a derby hat and Prince Albert coat at all times, even when working his claim. He gambled away as much as a thousand dollars a night in Dawson's saloons and frequently presented expensive gifts to the dancehall girls. The week before he had given Nellie the Pig a necklace of gold nuggets.

"Hey, Brian," Axel Anderson called. "I hear Constantine's put you on the wagon."

Several people at nearby tables laughed.

"Just for the morning, Axel. I'll be at the bar two seconds after this trial ends, you can count on that."

"It might not end as soon as you think," Axel said. "Not with Hannah Young talking for Rollo."

The conversation trailed off as each of us indulged in his own thoughts about Hannah Young.

Moments later the doors of the Bank opened to admit Captain Scarth, Inspector Constantine, and the prisoner, Rollo Moon. Another storm had begun outside and the three men's clothes were covered with a fine layer of snow. The Yukon snow is peculiar. It seldom falls wet or mushy. Instead it comes sweeping through the Yukon with a hissing sound, scarring trees and cutting men's faces. The temperature outside had fallen to thirty degrees below zero.

"We'll set up court over there," Constantine told Silent Sam, indicating the far wall across from the bar.

"Right away, sir." Sam grabbed his new bartender and together they quickly dispossessed a half-dozen people from their tables and rearranged a small area so that two tables facing the room served as a magistrate's bench with a witness stand to one side. Usually a slow-moving, taciturn man, Sam was quick as a cat for Constantine.

A place was made for Rollo Moon near the magistrate's bench and the prisoner was given a shot of hooch and a tin plate heaped with pemmican. He drank the hooch straight down and began picking at the dried meat with his fingers. In place of drinking I studied Rollo. I was surprised that little Rollo had found the nerve to murder anyone. The man had previously struck me as completely harmless. He was a tenderfoot, a *cheechako* in Yukon slang, who had come up to Canada from Seattle when the first rumors of the great Yukon gold strike reached the outside world. A man of slight build, receding sandy hair, and unshapen nose, Rollo's only prominent feature was a large Adam's apple. He had been a streetcar conductor in Seattle, hardly the kind of man to commit murder. But then gold had turned many supposedly timid and God-fearing men into killers.

A stirring among the crowd caused me to turn in my chair in time to see Hannah Young sweep through the doors of the Bank. *Sweep* was just the word for it, too. The damned woman never walked anywhere. She moved through the frozen streets of Dawson like royalty. Even on snowshoes she seemed to glide where others were forced to stamp holes in the snow.

"Hello, boys!" she sang out. "Good morning, Sam.... And a good day to you, Inspector Constantine.... Captain Scarth, you look very distinguished today."

Scarth and Constantine rose. Constantine even bowed slightly. Hannah flashed them a brilliant smile and sat down next to Rollo, putting her arm around the little man and giving him a hug of support.

At that moment I would have gladly traded places with Rollo even though it meant going into the dock for murder. "That redhead could have any man in this territory," I said.

"You're telling me?" Swiftwater Bill drained off the last of his hooch. "I offered Hannah a trip to Europe and a whatdayacallit – villa – for one night with her. She turned me down flat and that's a fact."

"She's been offered more than that," Commissioner Fawcett confided. "Antone Stander asked her to marry him. She turned him down, too. The woman's too independent by half."

Captain Scarth began hammering on the table with the butt of his Enfield pistol. "Quiet, everyone! Quiet! This is a court of law now, so shut your mouths. That goes for you, too, Deephole Johnson. And Sam, the bar is temporarily closed."

The crowd settled in and fastened its attention on Scarth and Constantine. Constantine cleared his throat. Like myself, he and Captain Scarth were dressed in elkskin parkas with pistols strapped to their waists. Constantine was tall and arrow straight, Scarth shorter and wide as a door. Both men exuded the stuff of stern authority. It's a manner both natural and cultivated by the North-West Mounted Police. With fewer than thirty mounties to keep the peace over the thousands of square miles of the Yukon Territory, our reputation was our most powerful weapon.

"This court is convened to ascertain the facts regarding the death of Michael Lynch," Constantine began. "Most of you know the special ruling by which the Mounted Police are allowed to operate in this territory. For those who may not understand, let me just say that the government in Ottawa has decreed that two officers of the RCMP* have the power of a magistrate in these remote outposts."

Constantine glared around as if daring any man to speak out against his authority. No one did. "Now you may also be wondering why Captain Scarth and I have allowed the court to be convened in these … uh … unconventional surroundings. There are several factors. First, this crime is more serious than most we have tried here at Dawson. Our usual punishment is a term at hard labor on the government woodpile or a blue ticket out of the territory. The punishment for murder is death. Second, Miss Hannah Young, who is acting as counsel to Rollo Moon, has insisted that the facts can be brought out only by holding this hearing at the scene of the crime. I yielded to her argument in this instance."

*Editor's note: The author evidently meant the North-West Mounted Police since the name Royal Canadian Mounted Police was not used until after 1920.

That admission by Constantine launched a ripple of whispers and chuckles. So even the inspector could be moved by Hannah's charm. I should have realized she was the only person who could have talked Constantine into transferring his court from the police barracks to a saloon.

The reaction to this statement caused Constantine's face to redden. "Let's get on with it," he said sharply. "Mr. Moon, step to the chair."

Rollo put aside the plate of pemmican and slouched forward to the witness chair. His doleful expression and the slump of his shoulders advertised his slim hopes for acquittal.

Captain Scarth went right to the question. "Rollo, did you stab Mike Lynch to death Wednesday night here at the Bank Saloon?"

The little man looked at his boot tops as he replied in a low voice, "Yes, I did."

"Did you have any provocation?"

"Any what?"

"Did Mike Lynch threaten you? Did you stab him in self-defense?"

Rollo hesitated. "No, he didn't threaten me."

"Is this the weapon you used?"

Rollo glanced at a knife Scarth put on the table in front of him. It was a crude tool, rusted and pitted along the shaft and bearing a large nick in the hand grip. "Yes, that's my knife."

"Did you bring this knife into the Bank for the purpose of killing Mike?"

"No, sir," Rollo said slowly. "I carry that knife for chopping ice and cutting bacon. I didn't come in here to kill Mike, if that's what you mean. All I wanted was a drink and some company."

"Why did you kill Mike?" Constantine asked.

"He cheated me." For the first time Rollo showed some spunk, lifting his head and looking directly at Constantine as he answered the question.

"Cheated you?" Constantine frowned. "How did he cheat you?"

"I don't know exactly." Rollo squirmed as he attempted to answer the question. "I gave him my poke. He poured some dust on his blower, weighed out the price of the drink, then poured the leftover dust back into my poke and handed it to me."

"I don't understand," Constantine said. "I've seen bartenders do that a thousand times, Mike Lynch included. How did he cheat you? Did he weigh out too much dust?"

"No," Rollo admitted.

"Did he spill some of your dust on the bar? Did you think his scales were rigged?"

Silent Sam Bonnifield stood up abruptly. "Now just a damned minute! Everyone knows my scales are honest. No one's ever questioned the Bank on that."

"Sit down," Constantine commanded.

Rollo was shaking his head. "No, none of them things. I can't tell you how, but I'm sure Mike Lynch cheated me. I've been swindled…hustled… outsmarted…ever since I came to this territory. And this was one time too many. I couldn't take it. Mike cheated me and I saw red. The next thing I knew my knife was in my hand and I shoved it into Mike's chest." Rollo put his hands over his face. "God! I don't know how he did it, but he took too much of my dust. I didn't have that much to begin with, so I could tell. But Jesus, I shouldn't have killed a man over the price of a drink. I'm sorry…dear God, I'm sorry.…" And Rollo began sobbing quietly into his hands.

Hannah Young stood and the crowd drew in its collective breath. This was the scene they had come for, the moment for which many of the spectators had struggled thirty miles through snow and ice to watch.

"Inspector, now that Rollo has admitted killing Mike and given you his reason, I'd like to ask him a few questions myself."

Constantine and Scarth exchanged a quick glance. They were touchy about the influence Hannah had already exerted on them, but her request couldn't be seen as unreasonable. Constantine said, "Go ahead, Hannah."

"Thank you." Hannah took off her marten fur cap and heavy mackinaw jacket. As she stepped forward she tossed her hair to straighten out the tangles and three hundred men ached for her, including me.

I had spent a good many long winter nights analyzing the way Hannah affected men. She was pretty, yes, and young, tall, firmly built with a longish face framed by tangles of red hair. But her eyes were her most stunning feature. Green and probing, they could strip away a man's surface toughness and leave him stuttering like a tongue-tied kid. Her eyes challenged you to live up to old expectations of yourself. And she had that bold way of moving, as if expecting seas to part in front of her. Hannah was ambitious, too. She bought, sold, and traded gold claims as if they were trinkets. No one knew whether she would come out of the winter a millionaire or a bankrupt, her business affairs were so complicated. Hannah drove tough bargains, tougher than any man in Dawson. But just when you started to forget she was a woman, Hannah would do some-thing softly feminine, like giving Rollo a hug to buck up his spirits or calling on a sick miner with a fruit jar of hot soup or showing up at the Aurora in a green dress instead of her usual pants and mackinaw and dancing with every man in the house.

She was a tigress and a kitten and I loved her. From the first moment I set eyes on her, I knew she was trouble. Vast, magnificent trouble, like the Yukon itself. And I have always been drawn to trouble. She had turned me inside out the way no other woman had ever done, but loving her would never do me any good. Hannah had made it clear a dozen times that she considered me a loafer and a drunkard who would never amount to anything.

Now she stood waiting for Rollo to get hold of himself. She showed no sign of impatience or disgust at Rollo's breakdown, only an attitude of calm concern. When Rollo finally did raise his head and straighten his back, Hannah put her hand on his shoulder and squeezed it gently. "It's all right, Rollo. Of course you're sorry for what you did. But you were right about Mike Lynch. He did cheat you."

"No speeches, Hannah." Inspector Constantine's rebuke was sharp. "Just ask your questions."

"All right." She fixed her green eyes on Rollo's face. "How much gold did you have when you came into the Bank?"

The little man shrugged. "Maybe an ounce."

"And how much did you have after Mike took out the price of your drink?"

"Hardly anything at all. Less than half an ounce, I'd guess."

"What grade of dust do you carry?"

"Commercial dust, like most everyone else."

Commercial dust was a coarse grade of gold liberally laced with sand. It brought only eleven dollars an ounce compared to clean dust, which was worth sixteen dollars an ounce. Most of the miners in the Klondike District used commercial dust to pay their bills. Some even salted their pokes with brass filings to make their money go farther.

Hannah did a little quick calculating for the benefit of the gallery and Rollo's judges. "So you gave Mike Lynch eleven dollars worth of gold dust. From that amount he was supposed to take the price of a shot of hooch, one dollar. That would be about one-tenth of an ounce. And instead he took almost your entire poke, am I right?"

"Yes, that's what happened. But I still don't know how he did it. I was watching him every minute."

"One more question, Rollo. How have you been earning a living since you came north?"

"Well, I staked a claim on Henderson Creek as soon as I got here, but it was a skunk. Wasn't worth the filing fee. Then I worked for Joe Ladue snagging stray logs off the river for his lumber mill. Now I'm doing handywork mostly. I made a few dollars last week salvaging nails from the old burnt-out Opera House. Axel Anderson bought them at thirty dollars a pound for building sluice boxes."

"Thanks, Rollo. You can go back to your seat now."

Rollo left the witness chair with everyone wondering exactly what Hannah was up to. So far she hadn't put forward much of a defense for Rollo. All she'd done was bring out some cock-eyed story about Mike Lynch taking too much gold for Rollo's drink.

"Can I call a witness?" Hannah asked.

"Of course," Constantine replied. "There were about thirty people present at the time of the killing. You know who they were. Take your pick."

"I call Constable Brian Bonner."

I went to the witness chair with a heavy stride to prove my sobriety to Constantine. When I sat down Constantine said, "I'd like to ask a few questions before you start on him, Hannah. Constable Bonner, did you see Rollo Moon stab Mike Lynch to death last Wednesday night?"

I nodded forcefully. "I did, sir. And I arrested him immediately afterwards."

"Did Rollo say anything to Mike before he killed him? Was there an argument of any kind?"

"No sir. Poor Mike had just poured a drink and the next thing I knew Rollo drew his knife and did for him in the chest. I saw the whole thing from over there." I motioned to a spot at the end of Sam Bonnifield's bar. "I was too far away to help poor Mike, but I saw everything that happened."

"Did you see Mike Lynch do anything suspicious?" Scarth asked. "I'm referring, of course, to Rollo's accusation that Mike stole some of his poke."

"I saw nothing like that," I answered firmly. I am a damned convincing witness when I put my mind to it.

"Thank you, constable. Go ahead, Hannah."

Hannah smiled at me and came forward with her hands in her pockets and her shoulders thrown back. It took all my self-control to keep my eyes from wandering to her breasts. They were dancing around like two cats in a bag.

"Constable Bonner, I'd appreciate it if you didn't refer to the late Mr. Lynch as 'Poor Mike'. It sounds as if you've already dismissed Rollo's story as untrue."

I grinned back at her. "Okay, Hannah. And I'll be glad to call your client 'Poor Rollo' a few times to even up the score."

The gallery burst out laughing and I winked broadly at them from the side of my face that was hidden from Scarth and Constantine.

Hannah continued to smile. If anything her grin was even wider and more friendly. "Tell me, what were you doing here at the Bank on Wednesday night?"

I had come prepared for that one. "I was inspecting the premises for fire hazards."

"Very commendable. Do you inspect the Bank for fire hazards every night?"

"Of course not."

Hannah put her hands behind her back. "That's right. I'm told that other evenings you inspect the Aurora or the M and M Saloon. And still other nights you can be seen sniffing out potential flames at the Blue Ox or Diamond Tooth Gertie's. I've heard it said that if the old Opera House had a bar, Constable Bonner would never have let it burn down."

The gallery roared again. This time I didn't join in. My face had gone hot with embarrassment and I knew without looking that Constantine and Scarth were glaring at me. Neither officer would have much sympathy for a mountie who laid himself open to ridicule.

"I do my duty," I said seriously, and was dismayed when my reply drew still louder laughter.

"That's enough!" Constantine drummed for order again with the butt of his pistol. "I've told you not to make speeches, Hannah, unless you want this court moved back to the barracks."

"I'm sorry, Inspector. I didn't mean to make sport of Constable Bonner. I was only trying to point out that he's familiar with the Bank and its employees."

I watched in amazement as Hannah worked her charms on the two officers, wringing a grudging smile out of Scarth in reply to what I could see was a totally insincere apology.

Hannah continued with her questions. "Tell me Constable Bonner ... Brian ... did you notice Mike Lynch do this ... ," and she pushed back her hair from her forehead, "while he was measuring out Rollo's poke in the blower?"

"I didn't see poor ... I didn't notice Mike do anything like that."

"Forget Wednesday night. Haven't you often seen Mike Lynch at other times brush his hair back like this ... " and she repeated the action.

Gradually I recalled that I had seen Mike push the hair out of his eyes, many times. "Yes, I guess I have. I suppose his hair got mussed up when there was a crowd at the bar and he was working hard. So what?"

"I'm asking the questions. I have one more. Did you ever notice the length of Mike Lynch's hair and fingernails?"

I couldn't resist the opening. "I haven't been in the Yukon *that* long, Hannah."

The answer drew another long laugh. This time even Scarth and Constantine chuckled.

"I'm glad to hear it," Hannah continued. "For the record, Mike had very long fingernails and hair. Those are all the questions I have for you."

I left the witness chair and returned to my seat at Swiftwater Bill's table more confused than ever. I could see no connection between the length of Mike's hair and fingernails and Rollo's reasons for killing him.

"I have one exhibit for the court," Hannah was saying. "Can I have it brought in?"

"Brought in?" Constantine was as confused as everyone else. "I don't see why you didn't bring your evidence to court to begin with."

"That might have been difficult," Hannah replied. "My evidence won't last long indoors." She turned and waved at two men standing just inside the front doors of the Bank. "Carry him in, boys."

Phillips and Crowley were two miners who sometimes worked Hannah's claims for wages when they weren't trying to coax the yellow metal out of their own claims. When Hannah waved they giggled like kids and went outside with their collars turned up against the wind and snow. They were back in less time than it takes me to polish off a shot of Perry Davis Painkiller, Phillips at the front and Crowley at the foot of a six-foot wood plank. A body lay on the plank covered with a canvas tarpaulin. The corpse could only be Mike Lynch, who had been laid out in the open behind the NAT & T warehouse with only the tarp to cover him, preserved by the sub-zero temperatures.

Constantine exploded. "Hannah, I won't have you turning my court-room into a three-ring circus!"

"I'm not doing any such thing!" Hannah fired back. "Mike Lynch's body is evidence and I demand the right to examine that evidence in open court."

"Examine it? Examine it for what?"

"I'll show you." Phillips and Crowley had laid the plank bearing Mike's body across the roulette table. Hannah went over to it and turned back the tarpaulin, revealing Mike's head and shoulders. Mike was a fine figure of a man in death, as he had been in life. Though with the face muscles contracted around his mouth, his teeth looked yellower than I had recalled. "I had Mike's body moved inside the warehouse this morning so he'd thaw out in time for the trial," Hannah explained.

"This is disgusting," Captain Scarth objected.

"What I have to do won't take long. Did you bring the pan and soap?" she asked Crowley.

"Right here." Crowley handed her one of the shallow twelve-inch pans that miners use to wash gold and a bar of Orange Flower Skin Food, a toilet soap popular with Dawson's whores.

"What the hell is that woman up to?" Swiftwater Bill whispered.

"I don't know," I whispered back. "But she sure as hell is giving these sourdoughs full value for their hundred-dollar tickets."

That was true enough. The Bank had become so quiet that even at the rear of the saloon the spectators could hear the faint sound Hannah's hands made as she lathered them with soap and water. When she nodded to Crowley he lifted a large pitcher and began pouring water slowly over Mike Lynch's head. As Crowley did so, Hannah began washing the corpse's hair with the soap. She had positioned the pan on the floor directly under Mike's head so that the soapy water flowed into the pan.

Hannah spent a good five minutes washing Mike Lynch's hair, shampooing it slowly, rinsing it, shampooing again, rerinsing. Not a word was said during the strange scene, not even by Constantine or Scarth. Everyone understood that Hannah would make whatever point she was after in her own way and in her own sweet time. Besides, the sight of Hannah Young washing a dead man's hair was an event to be savored in later conversations.

At last Hannah finished washing Mike Lynch's hair. But those who hoped she would now make her point were disappointed. Next she drew out Mike's hands and began cleaning the dirt from under his fingernails with a pocketknife. Once again the pan was positioned so that the dirt from under Mike's fingernails fell into it. She cleaned each of Mike's fingernails slowly and thoroughly. I knew Hannah understood the powerful impact her strange acts were having on the crowd in the Bank.

"Are you finished?" Constantine asked.

"Yes," Hannah answered.

The inspector sighed in relief. "Thank God. Perhaps now you'll tell us what that was all about."

"I'll do better than tell you. I'll show you. Give me a little room, boys."

Hannah held the pan out at arm's length and began rotating it gently. Gradually the pan dipped lower and the water began sloshing out. In two minutes Hannah washed all the water and dirt from the pan. Then she tilted the pan so that everyone could see what was in the bottom.

"Gold!" The word came from several throats at once.

"That's right," Hannah confirmed. "Gold. Mike Lynch covered his hands with grease so that gold would stick to them when he was making change from your pokes. Some of it would get under his fingernails. The gold that stuck to his hands would be transferred to his hair, which was also heavily greased. That's why you'd often see Mike running his hands through his hair."

"The slick bastard," Swiftwater Bill muttered.

"Give me your blower," Hannah said to Sam Bonnifield.

Sam passed it to her nervously. "I didn't know Mike was cheating people," he wailed. "I swear I didn't."

"We all know that," Hannah said. "Mike Lynch was a small-time chiseler. No one who's seen you drop twenty thousand in a game of cards without batting an eye would ever say that about Sam Bonnifield."

Hannah poured the gold from the pan into the scales. She adjusted the counterweight and announced, "Seven ounces. Mike would go home after work every night and clean close to a hundred dollars out of his hair and fingernails. Rollo didn't know that when he killed Mike, but he did know Mike had somehow cheated him. Mike probably cheated all of you at one time or other. I often saw Mike pass his hands through his hair. When Rollo explained what happened to him, the reason behind Mike's habit clicked into place for me."

The sentiment in the Bank had shifted violently away from "poor old Mike Lynch" in favor of Rollo. At my table Commissioner Fawcett was saying, "Mike Lynch never was any good. He deserted a wife and two children in Denver, you know. And there was talk about the way he left Denver; someone told me very confidentially that Mike skipped town with the insurance money from a widow lady he'd been seeing."

"Mike was a rat," Swiftwater Bill agreed. "There wasn't an honest bone in the man's body. I've said so many a time."

"I want quiet and I want it right now!" Constantine barked. He and Scarth had been whispering together while everyone else in the Bank had been discussing Mike Lynch's newly discovered faults. "Captain Scarth and I have reached a decision in this case. Rollo, you are hereby acquitted of the charge of murder. However, you did kill a man without very much *direct* provocation. You should have brought your suspicions to the police barracks. Therefore we're issuing a blue ticket out of the territory. You're banned from the Klondike Gold District for a period of six months. We have a mountie going to Circle City by dogsled tomorrow with some mail; you'll go with him."

"That's better than hanging," Rollo grinned.

Constantine and Scarth stood together. "This court is adjourned. God save the Queen!"

"God save the Queen!" the Canadians in the crowd echoed.

"And the drinks are on the Bank," added Sam Bonnifield, anxious to obscure the fact that his bartender had stolen thousands of dollars from his customers. A shout of appreciation and a mass exodus in the direction of the bar greeted Sam's offer. The trial was over.

I watched Hannah hug Rollo and offer her hand to Constantine and Scarth. They accepted it warmly. That didn't surprise me. What did surprise me was that Hannah next came up to me.

"Brian, I'm sorry if I embarrassed you in the witness chair. You made me sore, though. I knew Rollo had cause for what he did and I wasn't about to let him hang. You understand, don't you?"

"Yeah...sure...I suppose so." I cursed myself for stumbling over my words. But with those green eyes turned on me I found it difficult to talk straight. "No hard feelings," I said in a steadier voice.

"Good. And listen, I want to talk to you about something. Can you stop at my cabin tonight when you're off duty? Any time will be fine. If I'm not in my cabin I'll be down in the shaft. Just give a yell."

"I guess I can make it."

I had no idea why she wanted to see me, and at that moment I didn't care. It was enough that every man in the Bank was watching us and that several people standing nearby had heard the invitation.

"Here's a better idea," Hannah said. "Have dinner with me. I bought some fresh venison from a Chilkoot hunter yesterday. You must be tired of the bacon and beans they serve at the barracks. I don't have any vegetables to go with the meat, but I do have an apple left from a bag of fruit I bought off the *Mary Dwyer* last fall. Can you make it for dinner?"

Dinner with Hannah! I could hardly believe my ears. "I'd like that, Hannah. And I'll supply the refreshments, a bottle of Napoleon brandy."

That drew a gasp of surprise from her. "Napoleon brandy! I thought Perry Davis Painkiller was your drink."

"Oh, I like a taste of good brandy now and then." I tried to keep the swagger out of my voice. Hannah didn't go for men who swaggered, I knew that about her.

"Then bring it along, Brian." She smiled and moved toward the door, stopping to accept congratulations and turn down offers for drinks.

When she had gone I grabbed Silent Sam from behind the bar and pulled him into a corner. "I'll have that brandy you promised me, Sam. And I'm afraid I'll need the whole bottle."

"The whole bottle?" Sam looked stricken. "Not a chance." He shot a glance at his customers, who were doing their best to clean out his stock while the drinks were free. "Look at those thirsty bastards. Today will cost me a fortune as it is. I'm not passing over a full bottle of Napoleon brandy, too."

"Look, Sam. Hannah Young invited me to dinner and I promised her a bottle of Napoleon brandy. If you don't hand it over I'll find myself a nice piece of cordwood and just about bust this place down to the ground. The only thing I'll leave in one piece will be that moldy old moose head over the bar."

Sam studied my expression and knew that I wasn't bluffing. The fact that I had once actually destroyed a saloon in Circle City helped convince him. And then, none of Sam's customers would be inclined to stop me after the tricks Mike Lynch had pulled behind Sam's bar. He sighed. "I'll get your brandy. Just let me have one drink before you take the bottle. Christ, I need it."

George Whalley (1915-   ) was born in Kingston, Ontario, and was educated at Bishop's College; Oriel College, Oxford; and King's College, London. He is a member of the Department of English at Queen's University, having served for many years as the department head. The author of several books of poetry and literary criticism, he has, in addition, worked as a writer for the CBC. It was while working on a CBC feature program in 1954 on John Hornby's last journey that Whalley first became interested in Hornby's life. After carefully researching this subject, he wrote *The Legend of John Hornby* (1962), from which the following account is taken.

Since the time of the Arctic explorers, the Canadian North has had a particular attraction for individualistic and even eccentric Englishmen of good family. One of these was John Hornby who in 1904, at the age of twenty-three, arrived in Edmonton and from there made his way north to the Barren Ground, the vast expanse of almost treeless tundra that runs eastward from Great Bear Lake and Great Slave Lake to Hudson Bay. The Barrens dictated the roles that Hornby was to play, "not an explorer, a trapper, a prospector," says Whalley, "but a caricature of them all". He became, as well, an amateur biologist whose notes on the Barren Land caribou, recorded between 1908 and 1919, were a valuable account of the animal on which humans in the Barrens depended for survival.

Hornby's feats of strength and endurance were part of the legend: he was able to run for fifty miles keeping up with a horse, to run a hundred miles in less than twenty-four hours to win a bet, to go for long periods of time without food, to live for a winter in a wolf den. He told a friend that he wished he had been born an Indian, and his philosophy expressed native values:

> In civilization there is no peace. Here in the North, in my country, there *is* peace. No past, no future, no regret, no anticipation; just doing. That is peace.

"The Last Journey" is based on the diary of Hornby's eighteen-year-old nephew, Edgar Christian, who left England in 1926 to accompany Hornby on his adventures in Canada. A trip into the North, said Edgar's father, would be "a priceless opportunity for a boy coming to grips with the troubled world of the middle twenties". In Edmonton, the two were joined by Harold Adlard, a twenty-seven-year-old ex-RAF pilot. Particularly ironic, in the light of what lay ahead, was Edgar's assurance to his mother that he was "as safe as a house with Jack".

Other books about Hornby include Malcolm Waldron's *Snow Man* (1931), based on the journal of another of Hornby's companions, Captain James Critchell-Bullock, and Thomas Yorke's novel, *Snowman* (1976).

The Last Journey
George Whalley

Edgar Christian's letter of 9 June to his father – the last letter he was able to post – filled thirteen and a half pages of writing paper. In the blank half of the last page Hornby wrote:

> Great Slave Lake
> You must be sure to look at a map, so as to get a correct idea of our whereabouts. This country is rapidly filling up with white-men. With best wishes to you all. *J.H.*

After writing his letter Edgar turned in to sleep in the boat thinking "just how much Luck I am [in] by being with Jack"....

Edgar Christian's first journal entry after leaving Great Slave Lake was not made until 14 October 1926. The party was then establishing on the north bank of the Thelon, at the double bend in the river about forty miles below the junction with the Hanbury, at the place where Hornby and Bullock had gone ashore to inspect the timber site, the place where Hornby had often said he would come back and establish. There is no way of saying what they had been doing in the four months since they had started over Pike's Portage, or even in the ten weeks or more since they had left the note in a cairn at Campbell Lake. Within the shelter of the fine stand of spruce they had begun to build, where the timber was long and thick enough to make a small cabin, where there were signs of axe cuts thirty or forty years old – perhaps Tyrrell's. By 14 October the walls of the cabin were up, the roof was well started; all three spent the afternoon digging sand out of the inside of the cabin making more headroom by making the building half a dugout. As a protection against the northerly winter gales this was a sound precaution.

They were still living in tents – it is not clear at what precise point they moved into the cabin – but the first snow had fallen. The temperatures were still moderate though below freezing. They had set out a trapline and had not yet finished packing in from the Barrens the last of a caribou they had killed there. Hornby had captured a white fox alive, probably to amuse Edgar...; on the evening of the 15th they caught another – "a good companion to our other little captive". They were preoccupied with hunting; even work on the cabin was less important than hunting. Edgar was up before breakfast on the 18th sewing his moccasins so that he could travel on snowshoes to look for caribou; by the end of the morning the snowshoe harness cutting his feet forced him to return home. But in the evening "Jack returned... with glad news having seen thirty caribou on a distant ridge behind camp so tomorrow we all go out in last effort for winter's grub." But already they were rationalising their earlier failure; they must have decided that they had missed the best of the caribou and could at this date not expect the most desirable provision; for Edgar entered on 19 October, the day after the sighting:

> We all started out early to see if caribou were grazing still on ridge behind camp but were disappointed in seeing nothing for miles around & as a strong cold NE wind was blowing & caribou in any case having no fat on we decided to turn back & finish fixing up the house. Weather much colder all day but river still flowing. -8°F.

Next day there was a strong wind with heavy drift. Jack and Harold went round the trapline and found nothing. So on the 21st – "another very windy unpleasant day" – they developed films in the morning and in the afternoon worked at the house, particularly building the porch to protect the south-facing door. The house was small – only fourteen feet square – and once the sand had been dug out of the inside, the walls allowed between six to six and a half feet of headroom. The door faced the river and the south, looking down the steep bank the hundred yards to the river and across the river at the extension of the spruce wood there.

Beside the door they cut a small window through the logs; and a similar window in the east and west wall, each being only about a foot square because of the difficulty of providing an insulating substitute for the glass they could not bring. With sand and gravel from the hillside they banked up the north wall almost to the level of the roof as protection against the north winds which – though broken in their assault by the fringe of trees lying between the house and the open Barrens – could be expected as a pitiless accompaniment of the winter weather. The roof, made of light poles set across a double ridge-pole, was covered with a layer of shingle and earth, but the season must have been too late to hope that this could provide a frozen waterproof layer against the snow. The pitch of the roof could be relatively flat to save timber; for no great depth of snow falls in and near the eastern Barrens, and no excessive weight was to be expected on the roof. The stove, according to sense and custom, was set up in the centre of the cabin; furniture was of the most primitive sort. They built a small log storehouse to the east of the cabin, and put there the oars and ammunition and tools; it was probably intended as a food cache in case wolverines and other predators were troublesome. By the middle of October there was still plenty to do, even though three strong men could quickly put together, with axe and auger, the fundamentals of the house.

On 22 October Edgar walked fruitlessly around the trapline while Hornby and Harold fitted a door to the cabin and made bunks. Nothing living was on the move except ptarmigan. The next day, in better weather, they all walked out on the Barrens to bring in the last of the caribou carcass, and found they had left nothing of value behind. One of the traps held a wolverine – a "scratching, struggling & snarling, voracious brute"; they felt no compunction in killing one of these nimble powerful thieves who rouse in woodsmen the same unreasonable hatred that sharks do in sailors.

On 24 October Edgar found a white fox in a trap near their camp "by a mere fluke". The weather was none too good that day, so Edgar worked in the house and fixed up a hand sleigh "to haul logs or caribou". The first blizzard struck them the next day – 25 October – "snowing hard from SE with terrific wind" – which continued for four days. On the first day, Edgar noted that "Being in all day was like Sunday in civilisation."

Two days after the storm had stopped, the diary breaks off, not to be resumed until almost a month later on 21 November. Their need to hunt, and to hunt productively, was clamorous now that the heavy winter had set in. In the last seventeen days of October, with rifles, traps, and nets, they had taken one fox, two weasels, one wolverine, one whisky-jack (Canada jay), and some mice. They still had some caribou but that could not last for long; they had some stock of fish bait; otherwise only staples. They were not starving; but they had defied the immemorial custom of the North in failing to lay in plenty of caribou in September. ...

Almost the first note of real desperation enters Edgar's diary on 4 March.

> Things looking none too good for if we can find nothing around here in a day or so we shall have to move until we get meat and camp out.

The seriousness of their position – though Edgar does not say this – turned very much upon their immobility. If only they had had dogs they could have moved; they could have travelled at large to hunt, even though Hornby in the past had grown disgusted with the way dogs could spoil the hunt; they could have travelled – now that the winter had set all things firm – back to Reliance (though there was now no certainty of there being people there) or (if there were any prospect of finding any inhabitants) to Baker Lake. With dogs the trip would not be formidable: a week or ten days at most. And even if their condition were none too good or their provision much attenuated, one imagines that they could still have managed the journey given a little luck. The lack of dogs caught them in a circle: to travel on foot, either if the snow conditions were difficult or in a cold wind, expended too much of their energy to leave any reserve for the essential activity of hunting. Once clear of the cabin and its warmth and the shelter it gave to their enfeebled constitutions, they were at the mercy of the cold, debility, hunger. The balance was already so fine that one serious accident, the loss of one man's effectiveness, would jeopardise the whole party. There is no escaping the tragic conclusion that Edgar Christian, with the best will in the world – devoted to John Hornby, devoted to the death – though he was courageous and willing, could not stand the cold, could not hunt effectively and was therefore a continuous charge upon the other two. For Hornby to leave Edgar behind alone in the cabin was dangerous enough, as the accident that occurred in his first solitude had shown. There was no alternative now. Edgar, too weak to stand the cold, would detain the whole party if they all travelled together.

On 5 March, the Saturday after Ash Wednesday, Hornby and Adlard set out at midday for the upriver cache, the day very mild but threatening storm. They took "1 pot of sugar each & whatever other grub they have wil be what little flour there is there [at the cache] or what they hunt".

Edgar himself thought he was "well fixed here for several days": he hoped to catch something in the traps and so save what food was in the cabin. That afternoon he shot a ptarmigan "which made an excellent meal for tea". Next day the expected storm did not break. Christian walked for four hours over the Barrens looking for caribou but saw nothing, and had just returned to the cabin when Hornby arrived back. Edgar's entry is grim: "Jack…had had no sleep during the night [or] not much for as a wolverine had packed it [the cache] off & broken into camp.…Plans are now to go back to cache as soon as everything here is fixed safe & hunt from there as we are out of grub. Harold foot-sore with 5 days grub is waiting for us." Hornby had brought a hare back with him, shot on the way home: it made an "excellent supper".

During the four days it took them to get ready to leave, the weather grew a little warmer, though it was still as much as thirty below at night: some birds could be heard singing, and there was a whisky-jack about, so that Edgar thought it "a shame to have to leave in a day or so & have to camp out & hunt food". Finally they got away at 2:30 on the afternoon of the 10th, and had not gone far up river when Hornby found a wolverine in one of their traps at the bend of the river. Hornby, already carrying a heavy pack, put the carcass of the wolverine on top. The snow was soft; there was a strong wind; temperature just above zero. They reached the cache at dark and found Adlard disconsolate there; for he had shot only four ptarmigan and had seen no caribou though they had seen tracks on the way.

For this journey – his first winter journey of any extent from the cabin – Edgar took with him a small *Canadian Pocket Diary* for 1926 which he had bought in Edmonton: this would avoid the risk of losing or damaging his main diary. Under dates for January – the date correct, but the month and day of the week wrong – Christian made five terse entries in pencil recording the trip, writing them up more fully in his other diary after his return. On the 11th – the day after reaching the cache – they were tied down by a snowstorm. They rested and refreshed themselves by eating the wolverine. The day's rest was good for Hornby after the exertions of the day before; but Christian hoped they would be able to move next day "as we are now in Condition after Wolverine". Because Adlard had neglected to mend his snowshoes the day before, they could not get away until noon. It was a much colder day. They travelled west, spelled at two in the afternoon in a clump of trees, made tea, and saw a raven going north – which made Edgar think "Caribou must be on the move." While they were there a snowstorm came up and they could not see their way. During the afternoon, hoping to find the river, they walked across a lake – which must have been southwest of the cache. At five they sheltered in "a clump of heavy timber" and made camp. Here they had only hide to eat. Christian slept a little; Hornby and Adlard ominously refused to sleep at all.

"Seeing how conditions were in the morning it was obviously foolish to carry on," Edgar said in his large diary afterwards. The "Snowstorm was not so bad" as it had been the day before: at least they could travel. They were all tired from lack of sleep; they were hungry after their breakfast of boiled hides; their packs were heavy, and the snow soft and deep. They took turns at breaking the trail and so – after what they took to be eight miles of walking – reached the river. Here they spelled, made tea, ate some hide and sugar, and despite their half-exhausted state decided that it was better to keep going "knowing [that] we would have a camp fixed for the night if we got to the cache & also hide mat which we could eat". This prospect, unattractive enough as it was, was a promising step towards "get[ting] back home as soon as possible". This was not a strategic withdrawal; it was a full-scale retreat *sauve qui peut.*

They reached the cache very late that night. Edgar soon fell asleep, exhausted as perhaps he never had been before. But again Hornby and Adlard "did not sleep but sat by the fire all night". This is the clearest sign of their critical condition; for Hornby had said on an earlier occasion, when his own situation at Reliance was desperate: "Sleep is a terrible danger. Certainly there are nights when you *must* keep awake." They had had little enough luck in the past; they had none now. On the 14th there was "a real hurricane blowing". Unable to move out of the shelter of the cache, they spent the day preparing hide to eat and resting up. It was ten below zero that night. They had no tea left. If the snow did not stop and the wind abate, they would do well if they ever left that shelter.

Next day, the 15th – eleven days since Adlard had left the cabin, five days since Christian had set out – they were able to start at noon, using the hand sled. But they found the travelling "very bad indeed". They were all "feeling as weak & feeble as anything & intensely cold". Pulling a load through soft snow in that condition was a pitiless self-torture; but they could not risk another night in the open. By eight in the evening they made

a final dash for the cabin, dumping everything they could leave behind and going on "with bare necessities". On the last stretch in the dark Hornby "fell and must have hurt himself badly". It seems to have taken them another couple of hours to reach the cabin. Christian was incapacitated when they arrived. Hornby, despite his fall, was the only one in command of himself: "Jack was a marvel, light[ed] fire, made tea & cut firewood". The cabin must have been like a tomb, for the frost had been in it for five days. Christian fell asleep about 11:30.

Next day they rested, doing as little as possible, though Hornby went out and killed a ptarmigan. A peculiar irony awaited their return: "In our absence caribou & wolverine past close to the house...so it shows what a mistake moving from a warm house was." Edgar never referred to this again. Perhaps if they could rest a little they could get out and hunt. They needed something. Now Hornby, though "he will keep a-going and doing most work and [carrying] heavy packs," was looking "very poor". If their lives hung on a thread, it was not a very substantial one: for the calculated risk of a wide-ranging winter hunt for caribou had exhausted them. They were lucky to have survived that hunt. Unless their fortunes changed, and changed soon, they would never be able to move so far from the cabin again....

After ptarmigan were taken on 30 March there was an interval of seventeen days before they took any game of any kind. Their condition was now deteriorating very rapidly, and by the end of that empty period Hornby was dying. On 1 April he first admitted that his left leg, injured apparently in the homecoming fall a fortnight before, was causing him acute pain; perhaps (Edgar thought) a change in the weather had brought it on, but it prevented him from getting much sleep. But as long as he could move outside the cabin, he never stopped his crazy, scrabbling search for food for the party. He was almost certainly starving himself surreptitiously for the benefit of his companions. Unable to kill anything, he took advantage of milder weather on 2 April to walk out to the place where Adlard had killed the caribou in February and collect "a little blood which made an excellent snack". Adlard was now feeling ill, and found the effort of fetching wood and water almost more than he could manage.

April 4 was a turning point: that day Hornby made his last expedition to the Barrens – a pitiful search for the paunch of the February caribou.

Edgar, realising how momentous the occasion was, entered his diary twice that day.

> *April 4th.* I now write today's diary as far as it goes to make sure of it. Jack during night decided that as the weather seemed milder he should make an attempt to get in Caribou guts from Barrens as his leg is getting worse and he feels it is the last day he can move on no more grub than we have without eating Wolverine [?hide]. Harold dug up fish scraps and bones from bait pile and cooked them up. Meanwhile I rested and Jack kept on saying he would be all in and absolutely crocked when he eventually got home again and that we would have to carry on. What a mental strain it was. I felt homesick as never before and hope to God they know not what Jack is suffering. I rubbed his leg amidst tears and he had saved a little Fox meat for me to eat. This cheered me up, I suppose I was crumbling up because of no grub but still, by midday Jack started, all muffled up, looking as cold as charity and could hardly walk. I wish I could buck the cold more and share his hardships, but he has a mind and will of his own which no one else has got. I now sit here with Harold frying up bits of fish to eat and wait for Jack, who by now must be icy cold in the Barrens.

Five hours later Hornby got back to the cabin. He had got very cold digging in the snow and had not found what he was looking for. The attempt, though fruitless, brought release to all of them: "Jack feels content ... this makes us all feel better and more optimistic".

On 5 April they started burning logs from the storehouse because none of them was strong enough to cut fresh wood. Edgar found, after three days' abstention, that he was too weak to drink tea so gave it up altogether. Hornby was resting his leg after his exertions on the Barrens. Now the real menace came from Adlard. "Harold talks like an old woman all day in the house and [is an] awful worry to Jack who is the only one really suffering pain." At first Edgar could say – "Time moves on, each day longer and when fine weather comes Caribou more likely to come so we hang on, hoping for the best in a good warm house." But it was not as simple as that. With prolonged starvation, the circle of loyalty shrinks, until the horizon of the mind is limited to a dreadful apathetic self-preoccupation, exquisitely sensitive to repel any intrusion upon the inner desolation. On the morning of the 6th there was a sharp outburst:

> Jack had to curse Harold eventually to stop his carrying on and it was like water on a duck's back. He is very queer at times now and one must keep an eye on him at all times till we get grub. Poor devil must be feeling bad but we are all feeling just the same and I find it Hell to move around at all.

Hornby took a walk and looked unsuccessfully for ptarmigan on the 6th. They were living now on scraps and bones. For a couple of days he spoke of going out on the Barrens again, but weather prevented him. Harold Adlard – "Not normal today" Edgar said on the 7th – was plunged in self-pity and complaints. Hornby and Christian could scarcely stand, yet they watched Adlard warily, their nerves torn to shreds by his insistent and perpetual aimless movement in and out of the house, never still, never accomplishing anything, never finishing anything. Physically the fittest of the three, his resolution seemed utterly to be broken; afraid of himself, afraid that he had passed the limit of his endurance, he was draining from the others what emotional energy they had left. Hornby and Christian, in their affection for each other, and in the silent understanding that needed neither commentary nor emphasis, were much stronger than Harold Adlard: perhaps it was their strength that was breaking Adlard, adding the reproof of their endurance to the bitterness of his personal isolation.

Edgar Christian's resentment mounted steadily; but his concern was for Hornby who, collapsing on the 9th with the pain of his leg, denied Edgar the luxury of his resentment against Adlard and denied Adlard the luxury of his self-pity. That night they cut up "the best pelt of all to eat, a beautiful Wolverine"; after that they had four more but none of them with any food value. On the 10th, when Hornby was "looking very bad and speaks very weak and seems to be all in", when Adlard showed no sign of rousing himself, Edgar took a walk to the traps and found nothing. He saw two chicken hawks and interpreted these as "the first sign of Spring coming". Hornby, he said, still wanted to go on to the Barrens to find the caribou guts; but, Edgar said, "he is not fit at all and I hope to God we can get some game very soon. I can't last forever as I am, I am sure, and Jack has gone too far already." That night Hornby wrote his will and the two boys signed it.

April 10th 1927

The Last Statement
of John Hornby.

I hereby bequeath
to Edgar Vernon
Christian everything
I may die possessed

of & [come] all which
might later come.
April 10th 1927.

Witnessed by. Edgar Vernon Christian
and. Harold. Challoner. Evan. Adlard.

Writing retrospectively at nine the next morning, Edgar said:

> Situation is now very serious. Jack last night told both Harold and myself
> that he felt he was sinking fast and might pass away at any moment, so he
> talked to us as to what should be done. I promised him I can carry on for 5
> days on Wolverine hide, doing heavy work and hunting. Harold took a walk
> after Ptarmigan last evening which proved he can walk, so Jack has told him
> he must get on to the Barrens and dig up the Caribou paunch. I am myself
> capable but do not know even where they are and Jack says I must keep my
> energy in case Caribou come on the river in a day or so. Last night Jack said
> he could last a week if I would, but he had a bad night, legs paining and now
> he says that 2 days is the most. Harold kept the fire all night while in vain I
> tried to rest, but how can I now under such worry?

By 10:15 Hornby was in atrocious pain; with each spasm Christian was
afraid his heart would fail. They urged Adlard, despite a bitter wind
blowing, to search for the caribou paunch again. He left at noon, and after
he had gone Hornby cheered up a little, saying that "he will pull through at
all costs as he feels the food he now has is doing him good." In private,
however, Hornby was less sanguine, and wrote five brief farewell notes
one of which – the one to Edgar's mother – is dated 11 April. Adlard
returned four hours later with some frozen blood and the news that the
caribou had been moving on the ridges in some numbers, though he had
not seen any; and that he felt strong enough to go out again the next day.
So Hornby "had another meal with us and would simply insist on me
having some of his". He had changed over to Christian's bunk and was
more comfortable there. The weather was milder.

That night Hornby fared better and looked better in the morning. He
told Christian that "as long as I attend to all his wants he can pull through
but impossible without". Much now depended on Adlard who, true to his
word, went out on the Barrens again that day. At five in the evening, when
the air was very still, Hornby and Christian heard the sound of Adlard's
rifle. But when he came in an hour and a half later, he was empty-handed.

On the 13th Hornby sent Christian out to see if there might be a hare in a trap. There was nothing; and on his way back he fainted and reached the cabin only with difficulty. "Harold in same state", he said, "and also Jack". The trouble, they were now sure, was that they were "bound up from bones which we must have eaten 10 days ago". Adlard got out to hunt that day, but soon returned completely exhausted. Hornby was now determined – with Edgar's help – to clear his system of the bones, using an emetic syringe improvised from a test tube; otherwise, he said, there was no hope. Mild all day, the weather broke into rain that night, making the house more wretched with the dripping wet. Next morning at daybreak Harold Adlard was "absolutely unhinged", but the weather prevented hunting, so Adlard lay still "in hopes of hunting tomorrow". Hornby was full of hopes that he could "clear his system of bones tomorrow"; but Christian admitted that "I have never felt so tired as I am now and hope I can struggle through till tomorrow." The demands of the situation were so relentless that Edgar, after being up all one night with Hornby and having nothing to eat all the next day, still had to be able to look after Hornby and keep his diary. Adlard came in from the hunt at five in the evening, unsuccessful, and dejected. They had rendered two cups of jelly from the wolverine hide: this they shared with the prospect of watching all night over Hornby though they were scarcely able to stand. The end – for John Hornby – was not very far away.

16th April. After a very restless night and Harold and I both played out and weeping at times to see poor Jack in such a way, at 4:30 a.m. heard Ptarmigan calling. Harold went out and shot 1 after about an hour. Simply wonderful of him really, but alas, Jack is too far gone now to enjoy such a meal.

10:30 a.m. Jack started to sleep and fall unconscious so we can do no more just now. Harold and I so tired we can hardly keep a watch on Jack now. The heart still beating and breathing regular.

4:30 p.m. Between us have managed to prepare a meal of hide and rest a little. Jack still breathing but unconscious. Have got some broth from Ptarmigan in case he can take it at any time. Must now get out and cut wood for tonight and get water.

April 17th. 1 o'clock. At 6:45 last evening poor Jack passed peacefully away. Until that minute I think I remained the same but then I was a wreck. Harold good pal was a marvel in helping me and putting things a little straight for the night. I managed to cut some wood by dark, Harold promised to do the rest. He talked to me so wonderfully and realised my condition I am sure. I lay on my bed and listened to him talk and occasionally I dozed off feeling so worn out, and he kept fire during night and brought me tea and aspirin to help along, which was a relief as I was able to sleep. today Harold and I do just the essentials and I am looking over certain things as well. We both are very weak but more cheery, and determined to pull through and go out to let the world know of the last days of the finest man I have ever known and one who has made a foundation to build my life upon. Snowstorm all day. 20°. NE

That day and the next three there was a northeast blizzard – "as bad as any we have ever had in winter." There were many things to be done – small things – but they were too much for them; and "Cutting wood is an effort which seems incredible." Adlard was completely exhausted. On the day of Hornby's death, he had spent a long time "putting things a little straight for the night". The diary is no more specific than that: but this included getting Hornby's body down from the bunk and, with sacking and an old tent, making as decent a final disposition as could be. Then the body was placed outside the cabin, to the east of the door. Adlard seems to have managed all this single-handed.

Two days after Hornby's death, on 19 April, Adlard had to take to his bunk and could contribute little more to the task of staying alive. Edgar Christian continued to endure, tremulously at first, stricken again it may be by a desperate homesickness; then with a desolate resolution.

20 April. From bad to worse conditions go on. Harold is very weak indeed today and can hardly swallow his food. What is the matter I simply cannot make out, for I am able to keep on my legs and get wood on the same food of boiled Wolverine hide. Under the snow we remembered a Fox that died had been thrown, so I went out and dug it up to cook for supper. I hope this will do some good.... Poor Harold is thin and weak, and I am not so thin or weak, yet have been doing more, actually more the last few days as regards physical exertion. Whether I suddenly go as thin as a rake and unable to swallow I know not, but my goodness, something will go wrong if I cannot free my system of foul food we eat.... I seem to remain cool and collected now, but if anything might happen to Harold, God only knows what state I will be in, but of course hardships and worries have been so tremendous for so long now that I am prepared for the worst or best.... The weather is storming so bad that I cannot hunt and in any case there are no signs of Caribou or Ptarmigan around. – 15°F. – 10°F.

Now they deliberately restricted their diet: they decided they must not eat any more hides or pounded bone. The weather was stormy cold.

Christian managed to scavenge scraps around the cabin and bring in wood; he had little energy to look after his companion who was now suffering acute pain. On 25 April, in the night, heavy rain fell again, drenching the inside of the cabin to add a new misery to their squalid and enfeebled state. A strong south wind dislodged most of the chinking between the logs; and when the cold returned, the wind whistled dismally through the house.

The diary runs on, rather light-headedly at times, until eleven days after Hornby's death when Edgar wrote down the date – 28 April – but made no entry. Then there is a gap of six days before the record of Harold Adlard's death.

> *4th May.* Now I start in writing my diary again. Since I last wrote I have not had a moment, for Harold's condition grew worse, and so did mine. At 10:30 p.m. dear Harold passed away. After a bad relapse the previous night, he seemed to get better during the day, so I went out to cut wood and get water. When I came back he said he felt very queer and knew not what to do. He was in pain. By 10:5 he had gone unconscious and slept. As for myself now I am played out after no sleep and food for a long time so have managed to make up some soup from bones and have a cup of tea and rest. Today I must fix things up as best as possible, cut wood, dig in snow for scraps of fish which we are surviving on still and rest as best I can and trust for a good day tomorrow. I cannot hunt, as walking around in soft snow is beyond my powers now, and the weather is bad.

In spite of his feeble condition, Edgar Christian managed by himself to perform for Harold Adlard's body the same offices they had accorded to John Hornby – not quite so thoroughly perhaps, nor so neatly; and presently the second body, wrapped decently enough in blankets, lay outside the cabin east of the door.

The diary entries now become less frantic and taut, as though an intolerable weight of anxiety had suddenly slipped away from Edgar. His flickering power is concentrated upon a single issue. Day after day – sometimes at intervals of only a few hours – he records, with a miser's minuteness and a millionaire's detachment, the precise content of his larder. The struggle was no longer even confused by the question of hunting or trapping. There is no sign of panic. He knew there was plenty of food – of a sort – round about the cabin. He could hold on indefinitely – if only he could induce his crazy body to assimilate the miserable garbage he scraped up from the snow. He had watched his two companions die; he had weighed and considered all the symptoms; Hornby had gone over the whole thing very carefully with him before he died; he knew what he must do. If he could hold on, eventually the spring would come, and the caribou would come; then he could make his way out. Even fear had drained out of him now, now that he was alone. And now that he was alone, he could take one thing at a time. For a time he had wondered how he would ever get out of the Thelon alone. Even that question dropped into the background of his thoughts. On the whole his mind was mercifully numb, fixed upon a tiny pitiless cycle.

> *May 5th.* Today I resumed my digging and again had luck in finding more good food which had been discarded, 1 very fat Wolverine gut and kidneys, heart and liver, and 1 Fox gut, a quantity of meaty bones, and enough fish for 1 meal....I now have guts 1 day, heart and liver 1 day, meat scraping 2 days and bone boils to go along with anything insufficiently greasy....

> *May 7th.*...I felt much better, but to my surprise, I was as thin as a rake about my rump and my joints seemed to jerk in and out of position instead of smoothly. This I believe to be exactly the same thing as happened to poor Jack and Harold....

That evening he saw four ptarmigan feeding in front of the house – "the first things I have seen for a long time now". Next day, seeing that ptarmigan had been in front of the house again, he put two loaded rifles outside the door so that he could always be sure of a quick shot if need be; because now "Moving around seems to be a wobbly process." To go out and dig in the snow made his head hazy, his ears thick, his feet cold. The threat of snow made him "very worried and lonely hoping for fine weather". Sometimes he was ravenously hungry; at other times there was, to his surprise, no sensation of hunger at all. Then suddenly he would find himself alarmingly weak, would lay in extra wood and food, and den up for a day or two – if the weather were cold – to husband his power. On the evening of 14 May he noticed that it was to be full moon on the 15th – "and that's the date from which Jack said to look out for birds coming North. But there's no incentive for any bird or beast to come to this land of ice and snow just yet by the looks of it at present...." On 15 May he could hardly stand; on the 16th he started burning the furniture. Sun beguiled him on the 18th, but on the 19th there was snow again, forcing him to den up. On the 17th he had written "If I cannot get grub tomorrow must make preparations".

He entered his diary on 18th and 19th, and wrote down the date of 20 May. Then there is an interval, completed by his adding the date June 1st.

> Have existed by walking and crawling in and out of house finding plenty of food, in fact more than I could eat, but owing to its quality did not keep me going sufficiently to get rid of it as I ate it, being insufficient in grease I think. …Alas, I got weaker and the weather was blowing a snowstorm for 4 days; after that it wasn't even thawing in the daytime.
> Now June 1st. I have grub on hand, but am weaker than I have ever been in my life and no migration North of birds or animals since 19th (Swan).
> Yesterday I was out crawling, having cut last piece of wood in house to cook me food I had…but while out, I found fish guts and meat in plenty. At 2 a.m. I went to bed feeling content.…

At 9 a.m. on what may have been June 2nd he wrote:

> 9 a.m. Weaker than ever. Have eaten all I can. Have food on hand but heart petering [out]? Sunshine is bright now. See if that does any good to me if I get out and bring in wood to make fire tonight.
> Make preparations now.

"Make preparations" had for years been Hornby's phrase for doing the last things before death. Part of Edgar's preparation was to write to both his father and his mother: this he did on a sheet of writing paper brought from the Windsor Hotel, Montreal, as a souvenir of that gay holiday-like trip a year before.

> Dear Father,
> My address is not the above but I hope that this finds you one day. Jack Hornby always wished to see this country sometime before he gave up the life in Arctic Regions & wanted someone with him & I was the one this time I realize why he wanted a boy of my age with him and I realize why one other should come in order to make sure I got out safe, but alas the Thelon is not what it is cracked up to be I dont think. I have now been trying to struggle by myself for over a month & help my other poor pal but spring is late here and I cannot get fresh meat although have always had food to eat at times some jolly good meals only a few days ago which did not put me in condition to hunt fresh food but the weather blew cold & to-day June 1st has seen me with fine weather food but not fresh and unable to get fresh being too weak & played out. Adamson Corona Hotel Edmonton finds two trunks of mine In one that "Bible & Prayer Book" which Jack refused to let me bring. Do

not be annoyed but I know why now and Jack alone was one man in this world who can let a young boy know what this world and the next are. I loved him he loves me. Very seld[om] is there true love between 2 men!
Bye Bye now. Love and thanks for all you have ever done for me
Edgar

At the end of his diary, perhaps after writing this letter to his father, he wrote: "Got out, too weak and all in now. Left things late." Some time shortly before or after writing that he wrote to his mother on the same sheet of paper as the letter to his father.

Dear Mother,
feeling weak now can only write a Little sorry left it so late but alas I have struggled hard Please dont Blame dear Jack. He loved you and me only in this world and tell no one else this but keep it and believe
Ever loving & thankful to you for all a Dear Mother is to a Boy & has been to me
Bye Bye Love to all
& Dulc[ie]   Rita   Fred   Charles   &   Gwen
Edgar

When the fire had died out and he had decided that he would never light it again, Edgar Christian placed his two letters in the cool ashes of the stove, together with Hornby's will and the last letters he had written, and Harold Adlard's few papers, and his own diary. On top of the stove he left a note written on a piece of paper: "Who[ever comes here] look in stove." He was wearing a heavy grey sweater over a khaki shirt, grey flannel trousers held up by a silk handkerchief, a muffler around his neck, winter moccasins with puttees. He turned in to his bunk and pulled two red Hudson's Bay blankets over him, covering his head. The silence that had frightened him and made him homesick the first time he had been left alone in the cabin was now like wings folding about him. Perhaps he caught the faint sound of ptarmigan feeding outside. The sound brought nobody forth from the house with a rifle to try for an elusive target. The silver watch in the breast pocket of his shirt stopped at 6:45.

Born in England, R. M. Patterson was lured to western Canada in his youth by the "call of the wild". As a boy he had read Jack London, and had determined that some day "I too would travel and hunt in those blank, empty spaces of the Yukon-Mackenzie Divide." The claustrophobia induced by spending nine months in a German prisoner-of-war camp during World War I and three years in an office of the Bank of England prompted him to emigrate to Canada in 1923. With an English friend, Major Gordon Matthews, he spent the winter of 1928-29 hunting and trapping in Deadmen's Valley in the Nahanni country of the southern Yukon. In his reminiscences entitled *The Buffalo Head* (1961), Patterson describes the effects of that life:

> During the Nahanni years I had lived in a splendid mountain country and had the free run of thousands of square and very empty miles. That sort of thing gives one a liking for elbow room, and it also makes one intolerant of authority and the restrictions that are imposed by the presence of men.

From 1929 to 1946, Patterson was the owner of the Buffalo Head cattle ranch in the foothills of Alberta. He moved then to Sidney on Vancouver Island, "to an orchard and garden by the sea".

In the following selection from *The Dangerous River* (1954), the author recounts the legends associated with Deadmen's Valley. Today, more than fifty years after the two Englishmen travelled to the Yukon to root out the truth, the Nahanni is still a place of mystery and adventure.

138

The Dangerous River
R. M. Patterson

In the winter of 1926-7 I had to go home to England on some family business. The weather in London that January was even fouler than usual, so much so that it became almost a duty to stay indoors and try to forget the fog and the soot-laden sleet and the rain. So I came back from the City on this particular afternoon by way of Harrod's and picked out a book from the library there; then I took myself home to a blazing fire and a deep armchair – and the noises of London faded and I found myself back in the wilderness, following a strange, new trail.

The book was Michael H. Mason's *The Arctic Forests*. There were a couple of maps in the back of it – a physical map of Alaska, the Yukon Territory and the Mackenzie River valley, and a coloured ethnographical chart of the same area. The Yukon-Mackenzie divide, land of my boyhood dreams, was shown as a dotted line, named (inaccurately) "Rocky Mountains" and running vaguely between the heads of dotted rivers, themselves vague and their courses only guessed, north to the Arctic Ocean. Reaching up into the southern portion of these so-called Rockies, and rising near the heads of the Pelly, which are the furthest heads of the Yukon, there was a river. It was (inaccurately) shown as a straight line and it had a couple of tributaries; it seemed to be about two hundred and fifty miles long, and it ran southeastwards into the Liard which, itself, is the West Fork of the great Mackenzie. The river led into the country that I had always wanted to see (or seemed to lead there, for how was I to know that it was only on the map at all from the reports of Indians and prospectors?), and its name was the South Nahanni.

The ethnographical chart placed the South Nahanni in a large beige coloured area that ran all the way from the Wind River in the Yukon to the heads of the Sikanni Chief in British Columbia. The word "Nahanni" was written large over this area: a section of Mason's book was devoted to *The People of the Arctic Forests,* and I turned the pages, looking for this unfamiliar name. There it was: "Nahanni (people of the west)" it ran. "They are a hardy, virile people, but have suffered much from white influence. They are hostile to strangers, and many white pioneers have been done to death by them. This tribe was for many years under the complete domination of one woman, supposed to be partly of European descent."

That was interesting: and it would be fairly easy, I could see, to reach the South Nahanni; all I would have to do would be to throw a canoe into the Peace River and follow the water down north – down the Peace and the Slave and through Great Slave Lake to the Mackenzie. Then, at Fort Simpson, one would turn up the Liard to the mouth of the South Nahanni, and from there northwest into the lonely mountain country of the Yukon divide, the land of the wild white sheep. Sometime soon I would do that, I decided – and strangely enough I never doubted that I could, though exactly what I proposed to use in place of experience has since often puzzled me. I was extremely accurate with a punt pole and could place a punt where I wanted it to an inch, but the art of handling a canoe had been acquired entirely on the Cherwell and the Isis – a very gentle school of rivercraft.

I turned again to the maps: I could probably sell the canoe in the fall at one of the fur trading posts in the Sikanni Chief country and walk south, carrying a pack, the two hundred miles or so to Fort St. John on the Peace – there must be some kind of a trail. That would be some time in October, but it would still not be too late to build a raft and float or sail down the two hundred miles of river between Fort St. John and Peace River Crossing, even if I landed in there with the river running ice. And that would close the circle and bring me back to my starting point; I could either ride north from there on the old Fort Vermilion trail to my homestead, or catch the train south to Edmonton, whichever seemed to be the thing to do.

I had had a run of luck lately and I could afford to make this journey this very summer if I wished. The homestead would be safe; my nearest neighbour would keep an eye on it for me, and the horses could run out on the range. I began to measure distances on the map: tomorrow I would go to Canada House and see what, if anything, they could tell me about the Nahanni.

Late July found me poling a sixteen foot canoe up a mile wide river. The sun blazed down out of a cloudless sky and it was hot and still – a hundred in the shade at the very least. The brown, swirling flood glittered and flashed in the bright light of the noonday sun: it seemed to come from a bell-shaped mountain that rose in the west out of the flatlands of the forest country. From this mountain a steep, scarped range stretched away to the north and faded from view: to the south of it there was nothing, and no foothills could be seen to east or west of it. The range had been coming closer for several days now: it seemed to quiver in the heat of that blazing noonday, and deep blue shadows were already lengthening on its eastern face: it gave promise of clear springs and icy streamlets full of trout, clean gravel beaches and cool nights, and I urged the canoe towards it, longing to be clear of this mosquito-ridden plain.

The big, brown, swift-flowing river was the Liard – the Rivière aux Liards or the Courant Fort of the old voyageurs, the West Branch of the Mackenzie. The mountain was Nahanni Butte and northward from it ran the Nahanni Range. But I did not know those names then and there was no map to show them to me: all I knew was that the mouth of the South Nahanni, where it met the Liard, lay just beyond the bell-shaped mountain: there was a trading post there, I had been told in Fort Simpson, but it would not be occupied. There was an Indian village, too, they had said, but it would be deserted also; all the Indians would be away up to Fort Liard for treaty money and supplies. And that, I thought, bearing in mind the description of these Indians in Mason's book, was all to the good.

I had heard a thing or two by now about this strange river with the beautiful name. Hundreds of miles away, at Fort Smith on the Slave River, someone had heard that I was headed for the South Nahanni.

"So you're going up the Big Nahanni? Boy, you've bitten off something this time! They say there's canyons in there thousands of feet deep, and the water coming through faster'n hell."

"But people have got through, haven't they?"

"Oh, I guess they have just got through – years ago. But canyons – and sheer! Thousands of feet!"

"If people have got through, there must surely be some ledges or something where a man can tie a canoe and camp and sleep?"

"I don't know. There ain't many that have come back to tell about it. Men vanish in that country. There was some prospectors murdered in there not so long ago, and down the river they say it's a damned good country to keep clear of... "

And then there had been that man in the Hudson's Bay store at Fort Resolution, and de Meldt at Hay River on the Great Slave. They had said it all over again but with more detail. The Nahanni? There was gold in there somewhere – coarse gold and lots of it away up beyond those deep canyons. Deadmen's Valley was tucked away in there some place – hadn't I heard of it? A valley between two canyons where the McLeods were murdered for their gold in 1906. No man ever knew what happened to them, but they were found – at least their skeletons were – tied to trees, with the heads missing. Laugh that one off! And enough men had disappeared in there since then that it was considered best by men of sense to leave the Nahanni country alone. But there was another lunatic who meant to try his luck in there – I would most likely run into him on the way down the Mackenzie. Albert Faille, his name was; he'd been trapping on Beaver River near the outlet of the Great Slave and now he'd got the Nahanni bug into his head. Red Pant, the Indians called him because he always wore great, heavy work pants of scarlet stroud. He'd pulled out with his canoe just a couple of days ago, and with them red pants on him a blind man couldn't miss him...

I had seen Faille, a day or two later, at Wrigley Harbour, a little bay on an island where the Mackenzie spills out of the Great Slave Lake. There he was, a small, red-trousered figure on the distant shore: I had got my canoe and camp stuff loaded up on the scows of a mining outfit that was going down river, and we had waved to Faille and passed by without stopping.

But there had been no nonsense or beating about the bush, with regard to the Nahanni, at Fort Simpson. There had been a succession of drinks in the upstairs of the old Hudson's Bay house, with the sun pouring in through the low windows, lighting up odd piles and bales of fur and all the queer implements and contrivances that a hundred years of the fur trade had drifted up to this old attic. Spilled over the floor lay the mail and an opened case of Scotch, for the first boat of the year had just gone by to the Arctic. As we kicked the mail about and extracted our own I listened to them: they were saying good-bye to me for ever, and they became more eloquent with each successive drink. The Nahanni, they said, was straight suicide. The river was fast and bad, and if a man ever did get through those canyons what would he find in that little known country of the Yukon divide? Gold – gold without end, guarded quite likely by horned devils for all anybody knew to the contrary, but certainly by the wild Mountain Men – Indians who never came in to any trading post either in the Yukon or in the Northwest Territories. They lorded it over the wild uplands of the Yukon-Mackenzie divide and made short work of any man, white or Indian, who ventured into their country. Just ask the Indians here or better still the Indians at Fort Wrigley. Why, you couldn't bribe them with all the marten in the North to go back west more than thirty miles from the Mackenzie! No – we'd better all have another drink and be sensible and forget about the South Nahanni...

One way and another I had plenty to think about as I brought the canoe upstream on that hot July afternoon.

It was the McLeod saga, more than anything else, that spread the Nahanni legend – even to the extent of earning for it, at the hands of one enthusiastic press writer, the title "Dark River of Fear".

There were three McLeod brothers involved in the finding of the Nahanni gold – Willie, Frank and Charlie. They were, according to Jack Stanier, a veteran prospector of Fort Liard, the sons of Murdoch McLeod, the Hudson's Bay factor at that post and they were "raised as Indians".

An Indian of the Nahanni country had been helped and befriended by old Murdoch, and in return he had told the McLeods of an Indian working of gold somewhere away up the Flat River, the Nahanni's biggest tributary, and close to the boundary of the Yukon Territory. The young McLeods were fascinated by this tale of treasure hidden behind the mountain ranges which rose from the plain, ridge piled upon ridge, across the Liard from their home. They mulled it over from every angle and planned some day to go and see for themselves; it was not too far away, perhaps a hundred and fifty miles as the crow flies – though vastly further as he walks, and with an untold amount of grief on the trail between.

Their chance came, oddly enough, not at Fort Liard but when they were "outside", in Edmonton of all places, six hundred miles (again by flight of crow) to the south and east. Why they started from Edmonton we are not told: perhaps they had sold some fur there to advantage, or they may have been outside, working for good wages in order to finance the trip. Possible somebody grubstaked them in return for a share in the venture – but anyway, according to Charlie McLeod, there now began an Odyssey of the North that rivals anything that even Jack London's fertile imagination could bring forth.

The brothers hit the trail in January, 1904. They took the train to Vancouver and from there they took the boat up the foggy inland passage to Wrangell in the panhandle strip of Alaska. The salt water of Wrangell Sound is cut by the fresh water of the Stikine River but it is never completely frozen. However, the McLeods bought dogs and an outfit at the settlement and somehow got themselves freighted off Wrangell Island and dumped on the solid ice of the Stikine. They went north up the Stikine against the bitter winter wind that blows there without ceasing from the plateau to the sea, through the gorges and the sombre forests of the Coast Range, past great glaciers that crawl down right to the river bank in this land of heavy snow, and they came after a hundred and fifty miles of trail to a drier, colder country and to the little post of Telegraph Creek. They went on from there, north by east, and in time they crossed a modest little gravelly ridge, not too far from Tanzilla Butte, and the ice of a long, narrow lake met their eyes: the lake ran straight into the north for some thirty odd miles; its southern end was no more than half a mile away, at the foot of a little hill down which the trail wound through the trees to the shore. The gravel ridge was the divide between the Pacific and the Arctic oceans and the lake was Dease Lake; they were once more on water that flowed to the Liard.

Down the windswept surface of the lake went the little party, two men

breaking trail, pounding down the snow with their snowshoes so that the dogs could travel, and one man handling the dogs and the load. The brothers passed by old gold mining camps, long since deserted; then they came to the north end of the lake where the mountains begin to close in. They followed the ice of the winding Dease River for a hundred miles down into the Cassiar Mountains and through them into the rolling country of the Liard Plain. They came to the Liard, but their trail led north and they took to some smaller river – it may have been the Hyland – and they followed it for a hundred and fifty miles or more; and the days came and went and still the trail led on, and they had long since lost all track of time. They were in the mountains of the southeastern Yukon now; and that country can warm up in the wintertime under the southwest wind, or it can drop down with the north wind to sixty and seventy below zero till the aurora crackles in the black night sky, and by day a sun that is without heat peers through a drifting veil of glittering frost particles. And it can do either one or the other at any time, just as easy as kiss your hand.

Sometimes the sun shone out of a deep blue sky, warm and life giving, for spring was on its way back to the Northland, and the days were growing longer. And sometimes it hung in the sky, rayless like a ball of copper in a sky of brass: a circle of light would be round it, with blazing sundogs to right and left of it, and horns of light growing out of the circle – and it would be colder than hell. Sometimes the spring blizzards would take a parting kick at the McLeods, and sometimes they travelled under a sea of heavy, driving cloud, with warm, wet snowstorms clogging and soaking into their snowshoes. And when men and dogs were full of moose meat all was well, but when they were empty the cold could reach them through their mitts and furs and parkas, and things were not so good. And then they made camp and hunted ...

"We came to the MacMillan Range", Charlie McLeod says, but God knows where or what that was, for the only MacMillan Range on the map today is away west towards the Yukon River, three hundred miles from the Nahanni country. And in the end they came to the upper Flat River and there they found Cassiar Indians with coarse gold – "some big stuff", Charlie says, "up to $2 and $3 a nugget". Spring was at hand now, so they made camp beside the creek from which the gold had come, and looked the country over. Charlie doesn't say what became of the Cassiar Indians, whether they stayed or went away. From what took place afterwards one imagines that they must have gone: they cannot have been overjoyed at the arrival of the McLeods. The brothers called the creek Gold Creek. The prospect, apparently, was a small one – and quite likely the Indians had taken the cream off it. They panned for a while, and also used Indian-made sluice boxes which they found there, but the largest bit of gold they got was worth no more than fifty cents, and they didn't get much; they filled a toothache-remedy bottle with gold.

Then they took two of the Indian sluice boxes (which would be made of planks hand-hewed or whipsawed from local timber) and made a sort of a box of a boat for the run downstream to the Nahanni and home. They were about twenty miles, Charlie says, above what they called The Cascades of the Thirteen Drops, which is what we later came to know as the Flat River Canyon; so, in order to reach their home, they had to travel about a hundred and ten miles down the Flat River in their box-like contraption, roughly the same distance down the Nahanni, and finally eighty miles up the Liard.

They started off light-heartedly enough and tried to run the Canyon, as dirty a piece of water as you could wish to see, but at the first of the thirteen drops they swamped and lost everything, including the bottle of gold – salvaging only a rifle and thirty shells.

They went back to Gold Creek and got themselves a moose. Then they went to work, shifted some more boulders and panned out some more gold. Finally they made a boat out of two more of the Indians' precious sluice boxes, and made a trackline out of thin strips of moose hide so that they could lower their outfit down the worst places in the river. And somehow they got their crazy bateau safely down through the canyons to Nahanni Butte and home to Fort Liard.

Glad, possibly, to settle down for a while after this long trip, Willie McLeod went to work for the Hudson's Bay Company. But no prospector can ever permanently settle down: as he works at some humdrum job he keeps running over his last trip in his mind and building up new theories; he can soon see what mistakes he made, just where he took the wrong line and exactly what he ought to have done...

Willie soon had it all figured out to his own satisfaction, and in 1905 he set off again for the Nahanni, taking with him Frank and an unnamed Scottish engineer. There was a vague story that Willie had lost a large amount of gold "when his canoe upset", but that he still retained a small bottle, containing about five ounces, which had been held in a sash wrapped round his waist; with this, it was said, he drew the Scotsman into it. The little party disappeared up the Nahanni, and a year went by and there was no sign of them.

Charlie McLeod started a search for his brothers which ended in 1908 with the finding of the bones of Willie and Frank in their camp by the Nahanni. They were found in the mountain-ringed valley that lies between the Lower and Second canyons of the Nahanni: the valley was named that day by Charlie McLeod's party – they called it Deadmen's Valley, and to this day it bears that name.

The McLeods' camp in Deadmen's Valley was in the spruce on the left bank of the Nahanni, not far below Second Canyon Mountain. The dead men had been supposedly on their way out: one of them had always had a habit of leaving messages on bits of wood, blazed trees and so forth, and here, true to form, he had written one – on a split sled runner, this time: "We have found a fine prospect," it ran.

There was no trace of the white man: he is either unnamed, or referred to as Weir or Wilkinson. Nobody seems to know much about him: one version of the story traces him to Telegraph Creek with $8,000 in dust and nuggets, and another claims that the Mounted Police traced him as far as Vancouver, where he apparently had with him $5,000 in gold: from there the trail was lost. If this white man killed the McLeods and went out by way of the upper Liard and the Dease to Telegraph Creek and Vancouver, one is tempted to ask why the deed was not done up the Flat River near the Yukon Border, instead of down in Deadmen's Valley with all those weary miles to retrace upstream alone.

The murdered men were apparently shot while in their sleeping bags, one report says. And then G. M. McLeod, Charlie's son, steps in with an interview to *The Calgary Albertan* for February 19th, 1947 – a time when the press had seized on this old tale and had created a furore about the Nahanni and its tally of dead men. "River of Mystery" they called it, and by many another wild title, including that of "Headless Valley", for they had fastened onto that feature of the story in particular. The *Alaska Highway Handbook* went one better. "The jumping off point", it said of Fort Nelson, "for The Valley of Vanishing Men".

G. M. McLeod added some further detail: his two uncles were found and buried by Charlie McLeod. Their heads were gone and could not be found so "Charlie buried them without their heads." There were seven witnesses present and a cross was set up. "One brother was found lying in their night bed face up, and the other one was lying face down, three steps away, with his arms outstretched in a vain attempt to reach his gun which was at the foot of a tree, only another step from where he fell. The blankets were thrown half across his brother as if he'd left the bed with a leap." The murderer took no valuables, nothing but the gold.

G. M. McLeod should have known what he was talking about since the murdered (?) men were his uncles. The story is quite different from the one that I had heard at Fort Simpson, which was that the skeletons of the McLeods were found tied to trees and minus their heads. But there is something queer about both these accounts to any one with experience of the North: the story of one of the most recent tragedies of the Nahanni country will show why.

In the spring of 1949 a man called Shebbach died of starvation at the mouth of Caribou Creek on the Flat River. He had threaded his way through the mountains on foot, in the fall of 1948, from the nearest point on the Alaska Highway, some two hundred miles by trail south by west from Caribou Creek. His partner was to have gone by river, taking in supplies, but when Shebbach got to the mouth of Caribou Creek, mapping out in his head, no doubt, the wonderful feed he was going to have, he found nobody there and no grub in the cache. And nobody came, and winter shut down on the land.

He had come in carrying a .22 rifle and living off the country. Eventually his supply of .22 cartridges gave out and his diary became a record of forty-two days of starvation. Then he died. I had the story from Kraus, a prospector-trapper, who lives down by Nahanni Butte, the only white man – except Faille who is a nomad and whom no man can pin down to any one spot – to make his home on the Nahanni. Kraus questioned the forty-two days starvation period, but that is quite possible. When Jack Hornby with Adlard and Christian died on the Thelon River they lived on scraps, whiskey-jacks, odds and ends and bits of wolverine hide until Christian, who kept a diary and who was the last to die, had starved for over sixty days. Kraus, who is game warden for the Nahanni area, was sent up in the summer of 1949 to see where Shebbach was. He found him at Caribou Creek, but not all in one place – the bears had broken into the cabin and what had been Shebbach was scattered all over the flat – just a mess, Kraus said, scraps of clothing here and there and bits of bone that had been gnawed and dragged about by "bears, wolves and every other damned thing that could chew".

Deadmen's Valley is just as full of bears and wolves as the Caribou Creek country: how was it, then, that the McLeods were found so neatly tied to trees, or lying just as they had been killed and with camp so little disturbed, even to the hastily thrown back blanket, that those who found them could say exactly what had happened? For everything to have been in such good order the murder would have to have been committed only a few days, at the most, before the search party arrived, and that in itself would have been a strange coincidence, for it was three full years from the time that Willie and Frank and the Scotsman had started up the Nahanni. Not only that, but there would still have been a chance of catching the murderer, for he would not have had time to get out of the country.

To balance all this we have a statement by Flynn Harris made at Fort Simpson to a correspondent of *The Edmonton Journal* and published in that paper on December 23rd, 1929. Flynn had had a wide and varied experience of the North and, in 1929, he had been Indian Agent at Fort Simpson for seventeen years. He was very jealous of the good name of his Indians, even to the point of asking me, when I was going out in 1929, to go to *The Edmonton Journal* office and try to put an end to "all these damn fool stories about the head-hunting Nahanni Indians". Here follow Flynn's comfortable words:

> There's no denying there have been some sudden deaths on the Nahanni, but no Indians were responsible for them. The most romantic incident on the Nahanni – the death of the McLeod boys many years ago, after they were supposed to have located a fabulously rich gold mine – has never been accepted as a case of murder by men familiar with the river, though it has always been broadcast as such.

I personally am convinced that they starved to death and that the clues held up as proofs of crime were the work of wolves or other animals that discovered the bodies. As far as the gold is concerned there has been a good deal of talk about it – mostly by natives who are prone to exaggerate, or by gullible visitors.... In itself the Nahanni lives up to its reputation, however. It is a nasty piece of water, and an arduous and dangerous waterway for the best of navigators.

The Mounted Police are even more definite. In a letter to me, dated from Ottawa, October 27th, 1952, the Departmental Secretary writes:

> The McLeod case was investigated by the Force in 1909 and the conclusion reached was that they died from starvation and exposure. It was proved that they started on the trip ill-equipped and short of supplies, having only 50 pounds of flour and 5 pounds of tea when they left Fort Liard, N WT. The case was reopened in July, 1921, and further investigation substantiated the initial conclusion.

And in the same letter, in answer to a second question of mine, the DS went on to say:

> As to Jorgenson, we have no file or record of such a person being reported missing in the South Nahanni Country. In all probability a man by that name could have made a trip into that country and, like many other prospectors and trappers, returned to the outside safe and sound.

There you are and you can take your pick. But there must be *something* hidden away at the bottom of this well-muddied pool – and this something, whatever it is, must rest at least halfway between the calm official denials, and the gorgeous inventions of the outgoing prospector or trapper, inspired by Bacchus to a bewildering flood of traveller's tales. For my part I cannot see that a really effective investigation can be made of events for which there can be no witnesses – bygone events, the very signs and traces of which must have been blurred or wiped out, even for Charlie McLeod's party, by time, animals and weather. As to the five pounds of tea and the fifty pounds of flour, I question whether that means very much. It obviously would not last three men for very long, but they may have meant to travel light and live off the country and, if they had plenty of salt, matches and rifle cartridges, it would be easy enough to do that in that paradise of wild game. Scurvy can be avoided by means of fresh, wild fruit and by eating freshly killed meat only partially cooked: even salt can be dispensed with, for a time at least, by eating raw or very lightly cooked fresh meat. But if one knew what the McLeod's original plan was, that would help in reaching a decision: whether they planned to come out in the late fall of 1905 or whether they intended to winter up on the Flat River – in other words to what extent they were *overdue* when their brother and his party found them. But the case was officially closed and that was that.

That brings us to Jorgenson, the man without a record. Jorgenson was Poole Field's partner, and in the early nineteen hundreds the two of them had a trading post over in the Yukon Territory on the Ross River, one of the heads of the Pelly. The Ross and the South Nahanni head close together: both partners had heard of the lost McLeod mine and wondered what lay on the Nahanni side of the divide, and around 1910 Jorgenson went over to see. Two years later an Indian came in to the Hudson's Bay post at Pelly Lake where Poole Field happened to be. The Indian brought word from Jorgenson who had built himself a cabin some two hundred miles away, near the mouth of the Flat River and on ground that has since been washed away by the Nahanni. There was a map and a message for Field to come quickly – Jorgenson had struck it rich.

Field went, as soon as he could get away, by the same route that Jorgenson had taken – over the Yukon-NWT divide and down the Nahanni. He found the cabin burned to the ground and Jorgenson's skeleton lying between the cabin and the river: Jorgenson's bones were bleached, Field said, "so he must have been dead nearly two years." A new Savage rifle that he had taken with him from Ross River was gone. And the map had directed Field only to Jorgenson's cabin site and not to his prospect.

Poole Field – who later married one of Flynn Harris's half-breed daughters and became a well-known character on the Liard and the Nahanni – is dead now, and the above account is taken from an old interview in which he may well have been wrongly reported. Other stories were that Jorgenson had evidently been walking from the cabin to the river for a bucket of water when he must have seen something that scared him, dropped the bucket, ran towards the cabin to get his rifle and been shot in the back: that a rifle lying by his side with two empty cartridges showed that he had made a fight for his life: that he was found without his head but with his rifle and, conversely, with his head and without his rifle. Try and get at the truth of anything connected with the Nahanni in the old days – even the headless motif is dragged into it! To round off the Jorgenson story there is a report that Field found the Savage rifle in a store at Fort Simpson but could not trace the man who had traded it there – an unlikely yarn, since good rifles were not so common in trade nor the population so numerous in those days that a trader would not be able to remember and identify the man.

Other men vanished, quite probably through perfectly natural accidents such as the breaking of a trackline or the upsetting of a canoe, a broken leg, a rockfall, a disagreement with a grizzly...one mistake is quite sufficient when a man is travelling alone. And the Nahanni became a river that men avoided, except for the odd summer prospecting party – and the Indians and Poole Field.

Faille and I broke the spell in 1927. They said good-bye to us in Fort Simpson but we turned up again, and Faille has gone on turning up again ever since. He disappears into the wilderness of the upper Nahanni and no man, white or Indian, sees him; and always they say of him, "This time he's done it once too often." But he appears again, perhaps after two years have gone by, a little more bent but cheery as ever, and indestructible as bronze.

Then Charlie McLeod went back in to the upper Flat River, after an absence of thirty years, guiding three prospectors, and I went back with Gordon Matthews, and the news got around, and men became certain that we "had something back in there". A minor stampede to the Flat River was touched off in 1929: Gilroy's party was typical of this particular excitement; they went in travelling light, they had no intention of wintering in there and all they wanted to do was to find the lost McLeod "mine", pick up a quick fortune and get out. Gilroy told me a thing or two about the trip that may be of interest here. Gilroy, incidentally, was strong as a bull, square built with tremendous shoulders on him and designed by Nature for carrying a pack; he and his two companions, Hay and Hall, tackled the approach to the Flat River from a new and daring angle.

They went in by way of the Long Portage and Fort Nelson in 1929, and they were on the Nahanni by May. There their troubles began: late May and most of June is flood time on the Nahanni, and Gilroy and his partners ran into all the grief in the world. The brown, tearing flood was high, and it stayed high, and if ever it relented and dropped a little then, sure as fate, up it came again. On June 1st, Gilroy says, the Nahanni rose ten feet in four hours. The partners got through the Lower Canyon and Deadmen's Valley, and through the short Second Canyon into the Little Valley, and there they made camp on June 9th at Scow Creek, a small creek that comes in from the southwest. They had had enough rivering to do them for quite a while.

They decided, round the fire that night, to hit out next day up this creek that came roaring down past their camp, and to follow it until they got to the height of land between the NWT and the Yukon. Then they would travel northwestwards along the divide, shooting their meat as they went, until they found some stream that would lead them down to the Flat River near Gold Creek. And so they set out next morning, Gilroy and Hay carrying heavier loads than Hall, who believed in travelling light and had packed himself accordingly. The going was difficult in the steep, narrow valley, but evening found them camped in a little clump of firs well up into the timber line country, tired, tempers short and Hall grumbling about the slowness of the other two and the pile of junk they insisted on carrying.

The next morning Hall let fly, at breakfast time, with a few well-chosen words: if Gilroy and Hay wanted to make packhorses out of themselves, let them. As far as he was concerned, to hell with it! A rifle and a mosquito net would do for him and he would wait for them on Gold Creek, or wherever the stuff was, with his claims staked; and they could stake alongside him when they got there – if they ever did. And, with that, he slung his little pack over his shoulders, picked up his rifle and hit the trail. Some time later they caught a glimpse of him climbing, away up a long valley against a background of grey boulders, green grass and alpine flowers. And then they saw him again, once, silhouetted for a moment against the blue, summer sky – and that was the last time that any man ever set eyes on Angus Hall.

Gilroy and Hay travelled on across the alpine country, keeping above timber line by day and dropping at nights to camp by some small patch of balsam fir. They ate enormously of meat, and, since there was a limit to what they could carry and still make time, they shot an animal almost every day – mostly bears, Gilroy said. They travelled northwest, and eventually they dropped down to what they thought was the Flat River; but it was Caribou Creek, and they had to climb up again and cross another divide to reach the upper Flat River. Their arrival on the Flat was a memorable occasion. They were dog tired and they trudged slowly across a big river flat, thinking of all the nice kinds of grub that they hadn't got with them, wondering if there would be fish that they could catch for supper and swatting at the mosquitoes. Then they smelt wood smoke: a party of four prospectors had gone in by river, and they were just finishing supper when Gilroy and Hay staggered in. So supper was made ready all over again, and Gilroy and Hay blew themselves out, "till we pretty nearly burst", on all the things they'd been dreaming about. A wonderful bit of timing, that meeting was – a man wouldn't pull that off so sweetly and neatly twice in a lifetime.

The two parties joined forces and went on up the river. Somewhere, in a patch of hardpan, they found the track of a hobnailed boot – a right foot with nine nails in it; Gilroy took particular note of it. Hall had been wearing nailed boots and they thought now that he must be somewhere ahead of them, but they could never find him although they did their best, making big smokes and firing rifles from time to time. It was not until a year later that Gilroy told me of this: I explained to him that it must have been an old track of mine from the preceding September that had stayed fresh under the snow and had not been appreciably dimmed by the rain.

In the end they came to Gold Creek – a tough looking spot; boulders, boulders and boulders, little gravel and no gold. Floods and spring run-offs had swept down the creek since the Indians and the McLeods had taken the pay out of it years before, and nothing more could be got at without immense labour and a tremendous rooting about in the over-burden – if there was anything there at all. The odd thing about this venture was that all the upper Flat River country lay around these diggings, crying out to be prospected, and yet to Gilroy's party, and again and again to others, this creek seems to have acted as a fatal magnet.

Two of the river boat party, Hill and Cochrane, hit the creek about three miles upstream from the others and found the remains of a small shaft and a broken down dam, old cartridges and a whipsaw. They also found messages on a blazed tree left there by four men who had come there from the Yukon in April, 1921. These men had left a cache with some dog harness in it: under their names – Langdon, Rae, Brown and Smith – on the old blaze was a pencilled message which read, "Liard Smith and Indian arrived on June 15th, 1921," and then further writings stating that the four Yukon men had left Gold Creek on June 25th and June 27th, 1921, in two parties. Brown and Rae went on down the Flat River, blazing a tree at Irvine Creek and leaving a record on it which I found in 1928. Liard Smith was probably the Smith who lived and trapped in the lonely country on the Liard near Smith River, beside the great hot springs where the Alaska Military Highway runs today. Pencilled writing on an old blaze like this will remain fresh and legible for many years, preserved from the weather by the overhanging spruce branches and by a thin film of gum that runs over it as the tree seeks to heal the wound.

While Hill and Cochrane were poking around in the debris up the creek, Gilroy and the rest were further downstream examining old, grey, bleached sluice boxes of whipsawed lumber and a tremendous upheaval of boulders: this may have been the spot where the McLeods got their gold and built their box-like boats in 1905. But they found nothing else in the country to keep them there: a few colours of gold here and there, but that was all. Summer merged into fall, and they dropped down river and picked up the other boat at Scow Creek and went out – six now, out of the seven who had started, for the Nahanni had exacted a toll of one.

Then, in 1931, Phil Powers went in to trap on the Flat River and failed to appear when the ice went out in the spring. Constable Martin, Special Constable Edwards, Poole Field and Faille were sent in to look for him, for it was no longer 1905: the RCMP were in charge of the country now, and they like to keep a tidy record of the missing. In the fall of 1932 the search party found Power's burned cabin up the Flat, about thirty miles from Gold Creek, and his charred skeleton. There was only one odd thing about that find, but it was decidedly odd: the signs showed that the fire occurred at the beginning of the winter of 1931, but, nailed to one of the uprights of the cache, was a piece of paper with the words: "Phil Powers finished Aug, 1932."

By 1933 Canada was in the depths of the depression of the Thirties: nobody had any money, and men and airlines (which were then starting up and having a very tough time making ends meet) were desperate for work and freight. Gold was high, it was the one stable thing in a collapsing world, and the magic word could be relied upon to start a bunch of optimists stampeding in any direction. Conditions were ideal for trotting out the McLeod story once again. We were about to hear more of the same old creek up the Flat River.

This time the yarn was complete, even down to the inevitable map and dream. The map was produced by Father Turcotte of the Oblate Fathers at Fort Liard. It had been given to him, many years previously, by Father Gouet who was as much of a trader and prospector as he was a priest, and by Willie McLeod. The map had lain forgotten among Father Turcotte's papers: the word "gold" was on it in two places and the Father gave it to Jack Stanier, the old prospector of Fort Liard.

Stanier roped D – (wrong initial), an employee or ex-employee of the Hudson's Bay Company into it and the pair of them got themselves flown in to a lake on the Flat River. They came out with some placer gold in their possession: and here, according to the published story, Stanier was indeed fortunate to have chosen D – as his companion. D –, it would seem, could see further through a stone wall than most, as the old saying went; and one night, when things were not looking too bright for our prospectors, he dreamed a dream. The next morning they went up the creek: round a bend they came to a barren looking spot: from the wall of the gulch on one side a slide of rock and gravel had come down, and out of the slide stuck some unnatural looking pieces of wood. D – rushed forward: "That's the place," he cried – and, by God's truth, it *was* the place and those were the pick and shovel handles of the long dead McLeods! Most remarkable!

"You can kick the gravel heaps," one newspaper said, "and see the gold gleaming like butter." Nobody, of course, wanted to stop and consider why all this wealth had remained unnoticed by previous parties: off went the usual collection of hopefuls headed by the dog-musher, Harry McGurran, who had hauled the winter mail on the Mackenzie for many years – and river freighters and a certain airline had work for a while. The excitement was maintained for a little time by odd paragraphs in the Edmonton papers to the effect that "the Nahanni gold fields are yielding good pay," but inevitably it fizzled out and peace came again to the Flat River, and the moose and the caribou were once more free to breed and restock the country unmolested by men.

After this brief interval of romantic buffoonery things got back to normal. Faille came and went, and sometimes others would come too: and sometimes the Nahanni, the green, shadowy, driving river, would stir a little in its dreams and reach out and take its toll: in 1936 Eppler and Mulholland disappeared and, in 1940, Holmberg – and Shebbach starved to death in 1949, at Caribou Creek. And there were others, too. As Flynn Harris truly said, "The Nahanni is a nasty piece of water, and an arduous and dangerous waterway for the best of navigators."

Rudy Wiebe (1934-   ) is a native of Saskatchewan, the son of Mennonite settlers who emigrated from Russia in 1930. He was educated at a Mennonite high school in Coaldale, at the University of Alberta, the University of Tübingen in West Germany, and the Mennonite Brethren Bible College in Winnipeg. He is now a professor of English at the University of Alberta.

His novels and short stories are characterized by a vivid representation of minority points of view – Mennonite, Indian, Eskimo, Métis, and "poor white". Relying on factual data gained from books, pamphlets, government records, diaries, museum artifacts, personal interviews, letters, speeches, newspapers, maps, memoirs, and historical and geographic sites, Wiebe creates a view of Canadian history that is not normally found in textbooks. In *Canada Writes,* he defines his authorial role:

> I believe that the worlds of fiction – story – should provide pleasure of as many kinds as possible to the reader; I believe fiction must be precisely, particularly rooted in a particular place, in particular people; I believe writing fiction is as serious, as responsible an activity as I can ever perform. Therefore in my fiction I try to explore the world that I know: the land and people of western Canada, from my particular world view: a radical Jesus-oriented Christianity.

This view of fiction may be seen clearly in his novels, which include *Peace Shall Destroy Many* (1962); *The Blue Mountains of China* (1970); *The Temptations of Big Bear* (1973), which won a Governor General's Award; and *The Scorched-Wood People* (1977).

"The Naming of Albert Johnson" is taken from a short story collection, *Where Is the Voice Coming From?* (1974). The story is based on the life of an eccentric loner who sought peace and solitude in the northern wilderness. According to historical accounts, Albert Johnson appeared at the Ross River Post in the Yukon on August 21, 1927, a man in his early thirties with remarkably green eyes, a large wad of bills, and a misanthropic disposition. Within five years the man who valued privacy above all else became notorious as "The Mad Trapper", "The Attila of the Arctic", and "The Sadist of the Snows". Now, nearly fifty years after his death, he has become something of a Canadian folk hero, commemorated in ballads, movies, the names of bars, and in such "true adventure stories" as Thomas P. Kelly's *Rat River Trapper* (1972) and Dick North's *The Mad Trapper of Rat River* (1972).

Using the technique of retrospective narration, Rudy Wiebe has sought an explanation for Johnson's violence in the folklore associated with naming. According to Sir James Frazer in *The Golden Bough:*

> Primitive man regards his name as a vital portion of himself and takes care of it accordingly. Thus, for example, the North American Indian "regards his name, not as a mere label, but as a distinct part of his personality".

One's real name had to be concealed less evil-disposed people use it to cause injury. Wiebe's Johnson is a victim as well as a villain, a man whose sheer will to survive arouses admiration and pity.

The Naming of Albert Johnson
Rudy Wiebe

1. *The Eagle River, Yukon:* Wednesday, February 17, 1932
                                    Tuesday, February 16

There is arctic silence at last, after the long snarl of rifles. As if all the stubby trees within earshot had finished splitting in the cold. Then the sound of the airplane almost around the river's bend begins to return, turning as tight a spiral as it may up over bank and trees and back down, over the man crumpled on the bedroll, over the frantic staked dog teams, spluttering, down, glancing down off the wind-ridged river. Tail leaping, almost cartwheeling over its desperate roar for skis, immense sound rocketing from that bouncing black dot on the level glare but stopped finally, its prop whirl staggering motionless just behind the man moving inevitably forward on snowshoes, not looking back, step by step up the river with his rifle ready. Hesitates, lifts one foot, then the other, stops, and moves forward again to the splotch in the vast whiteness before him.

The pack is too huge, and apparently worried by rats with very long, fine teeth. Behind it a twisted body. Unbelievably small. One outflung hand still clutching a rifle, but no motion, nothing, the airplane dead and only the distant sounds of dogs somewhere, of men moving at the banks of the river. The police rifle points down, steadily extending the police arm until it can lever the body, already stiffening, up. A red crater for hip. As if one small part of that incredible toughness had rebelled at last, exploded red out of itself, splattering itself with itself when everything but itself was at last unreachable. But the face is turning up. Rime and clots of snow ground into whiskers, the fur hat hurled somewhere by bullets perhaps and the whipped cowlick already a mat frozen above half-open eyes showing only white, nostrils flared, the concrete face wiped clean of everything but snarl. Freezing snarl and teeth. As if the long clenched jaws had tightened down beyond some ultimate cog and openly locked their teeth into their own torn lips in one final wordlessly silent scream.

The pilot blunders up, gasping, "By god, we got the son of a bitch!", stumbles across the back of the snowshoes, and recovers beside the policeman. Gagging a little, "My g – ." All that sudden colour propped up by the rifle barrel on the otherwise white snow. And the terrible face.

The one necessary bullet, in the spine where its small entry cannot be seen at this moment, and was never felt as six others were, knocked the man face down in the snow. Though that would never loosen his grip on his rifle. The man had been working himself over on his side, not concerned as it seemed for the bullets singing to him from the level drifts in front of him or the trees on either bank. With his left hand he was reaching into his coat pocket to reload his Savage 30-30, almost warm on the inside of his other bare hand, and he knew as every good hunter must that he had exactly thirty-nine bullets left besides the one hidden under the rifle's butt plate. If they moved in any closer he also had the Winchester .22 with sixty-four bullets, and closer still there would be the sawed-off shotgun, though he had only a few shells left, he could not now be certain exactly how many. He had stuffed snow tight into the hole where one or perhaps even two shells had exploded in his opposite hip pocket. A man could lose his blood in a minute from a hole that size but the snow was still white and icy the instant he had to glance at it, packing it in. If they had got him there before forcing him down behind his pack in the middle of the river, he could not have moved enough to pull out of the pack straps, leave alone get behind it for protection. Bullets twitch it, whine about his tea tin like his axe handle snapping once at his legs as he ran from the eastern river bank too steep to clamber up, a very bad mistake to have to discover after spending several minutes and a hundred yards of strength running his snowshoes towards it. Not a single rock, steep and bare like polished planks. But he had gained a little on them, he saw that as he curved without stopping towards the centre of the river and the line of trees beyond it. That bank is easily climbed, he knows because he climbed it that morning, but all the dogs and men so suddenly around the hairpin turn surprised him toward the nearest bank, and he sees the teams spreading to outflank

him, three towards the low west bank. And two of them bending over the one army radioman he got.

Instantly the man knew it was the river that had betrayed him. He had outlegged their dogs and lost the plane time and again on glare-ice and in fog, and brush and between the endless trails of caribou herds, but the sluggish loops of this river doubling back on itself have betrayed him. It is his own best move, forward and then back, circle forward and farther back, backwards, so the ones following his separate tracks will suddenly confront each other in cursing bewilderment. But this river, it cannot be named the Porcupine, has outdoubled him. For the dogs leaping towards him around the bend, the roaring radioman heaving at his sled, scrabbling for his rifle, that is clearly what he saw when he climbed the tree on the far bank, one of the teams he saw then across a wide tongue of land already ahead of him, as it seemed, and he started back to get further behind them before he followed and picked them off singly in whatever tracks of his they thought they were following. These dogs and this driver rounding to face him as he walks so carefully backwards in his snowshoes on the curve of his own tracks.

Whatever this river is spiralling back into the Yukon hills, his rifle will not betray him. Words are bellowing out of the racket of teams hurtling around the bend. His rifle speaks easily, wordlessly to the army radioman kneeling, sharpshooter position, left elbow propped on left knee. The sights glided together certain and deadly, and long before the sound had returned that one kneeling was already flung back clean as frozen wood bursting at his axe.

He has not eaten, he believes it must be two days, and the rabbit tracks are so old they give no hope for his snares. The squirrel burrow may be better. He is scraping curls from tiny spruce twigs, watching them tighten against the lard pail, watching the flames as it seems there licking the tin blacker with their gold tongues. The fire lives with him, and he will soon examine the tinfoil of matches in his pocket, and the tinfoil bundle in his pack, and also the other two paper-wrapped packages. That must be done daily, if possible. The pack, unopened, with the .22 laced to its side is between his left shoulder and the snow hollow; the moosehides spread under and behind him; the snowshoes stuck erect into the snow on the right, the long axe lying there and the rifle also, in its cloth cover but on the moose hide pouch. He has already worked carefully on his feet, kneading as much of the frost out of one and then the other as he can before the fire though two toes on the left are black and the heel of the right is rubbed raw. Bad lacing when he walked backwards, and too numb for him to notice. The one toe can only be kept another day, perhaps, but he has only a gun-oily rag for his heel. Gun oil? Spruce gum? Wait. His feet are wrapped and ready to move if necessary and he sits watching warmth curl around the pail. Leans his face down into it. Then he puts the knife away in his clothes and pulls out a tiny paper. His hard fingers unfold it carefully, he studies the crystals a moment, and then as the flames tighten the blackened spirals of spruce he pours that into the steaming pail. He studies the paper, the brownness of it; the suggestion of a word beginning, or perhaps ending, that shines through its substance. He lowers it steadily then until it darkens, smiling as a spot of deep brown breaks through the possible name and curls back a black empty circle towards his fingers. He lets it go, feeling warmth like a massage in its final flare and dying. There is nothing left but a smaller fold of pepper and a bag of salt so when he drinks it is very slowly, letting each mouthful move for every part of his tongue to hold a moment this last faint sweetness.

He sits in the small yellow globe created by fire. Drinking. The wind breathes through the small spruce, his body rests motionlessly; knowing that dug into the snow with drifts and spruce tips above him they could see his smokeless fire only if they flew directly over him. And the plane cannot fly at night. They are somewhere very close now, and their plane less than a few minutes behind. It has flown straight in an hour, again and again, all he had overlaid with tangled tracks in five weeks, but the silent land is what it is. He is now resting motionlessly. And waiting.

And the whiskey-jacks are suddenly there. He had not known them before to come after dark, but grey and white tipped with black they fluffed themselves at the grey edge of his light, watching, and then one hopped two hops. Sideways. The first living thing he had seen since the caribou. But he reaches for the bits of babiche he had cut and rubbed in salt, laid ready on the cloth of the rifle butt. He throws, the draggle-tail is gone but the other watches, head cocked, then jumps so easily the long space his stiff throw had managed, and the bit is gone. He does not move his body, tosses another bit, and another, closer, closer, and then draggle-tail is there scrabbling for the bit, and he twitches the white string lying beside the bits of babiche left by the rifle, sees the bigger piece tug from the snow and draggle-tail leap to it. Gulp. He tugs, feels the slight weight as the thread lifts from the snow in the firelight, and now the other is gone while draggle-tail comes toward him inevitably, string pulling the beak soundlessly a-gap, wings desperate in snow, dragged between rifle and fire into the waiting claw of his hand. He felt the bird's blood beat against his palm, the legs and tail and wings thud an instant, shuddering and then limp between his relentless fingers.

Wings. Noiselessly he felt the beautiful muscles shift, slip over bones delicate as twigs. He could lope circles around any dogs they set on his trail but that beast labelled in letters combing the clouds, staring everywhere until its roar suddenly blundered up out of a canyon or over a ridge, laying its relentless shadow like words on the world: he would have dragged every tree in the Yukon together to build a fire and boil that. Steel pipes and canvas and wires and name, that stinking noise. In the silence under the spruce he skims the tiny fat bubbles from the darkening soup; watches them coagulate yellow on the shavings. Better than gun oil, or gum. He began to unwrap his feet again but listening, always listening. The small furrow of the bird pointed toward him in the snow.

2. *The Richardson Mountains, NWT:* Tuesday, February 9, 1932
                                      Saturday, January 30

Though it means moving two and three miles to their one, the best trail to confuse them in the foothill ravines was a spiral zigzag. West of the mountains he has not seen them; he has outrun them so far in crossing the Richardson Mountains during the blizzard that when he reaches a river he thought it must be the Porcupine because he seems at last to be inside something that is completely alone. But the creeks draining east lay in seemingly parallel but eventually converging canyons with tundra plateaus glazed under wind between them, and when he paused on one leg of his zag he sometimes saw them, across one plateau or in a canyon, labouring with their dogs and sleds as it seems ahead of him. In the white scream of the mountain pass where no human being has ever ventured in winter he does not dare pause to sleep for two days and the long night between them, one toe and perhaps another frozen beyond saving and parts of his face dead, but in the east he had seen the trackers up close, once been above them and watched them coming along his trails towards each other unawares out of two converging canyons with their sleds and drivers trailing, and suddenly round the cliff to face each other in cursing amazement. He was far enough not to hear their words as they heated water for tea, wasting daylight minutes, beating their hands to keep warm.

The police drive the dog teams now, and the Indians sometimes; the ones who can track him on the glazed snow, through zags and bends, always wary of ambush, are the two army radiomen. One of the sleds is loaded with batteries when it should be food, but they sniff silently along his tracks, loping giant circles ahead of the heaving dogs and swinging arms like semaphores when they find a trail leading as it seems directly back towards the sleds they have just left. He would not have thought them so relentless at unravelling his trails, these two who every morning tried to raise the police on their frozen radio, and when he was convinced they would follow him as certainly as Millen and the plane roared up, dropping supplies, it was time to accept the rising blizzard over the mountains and find at last, for certain, the Porcupine River.

It is certainly Millen who brought the plane north just before the blizzard, and it was Millen who saw his smoke and heard him coughing, whistling in that canyon camp hidden in trees under a cliff so steep he has to chop handholds in the frozen rock to get out of there. Without dynamite again, or bombs, they could not dig him out; even in his unending alert his heart jerks at the sound of what was a foot slipping against a frozen tree up the ridge facing him. His rifle is out of its sheath, the shell racking home in the cold like precise steel biting. There is nothing more; an animal? A tree bursting? He crouches motionless, for if they are there they should be all around him, perhaps above on the cliff, and he will not move until he knows. Only the wind worrying spruce and snow, whining wordlessly. There, twenty yards away a shadow moves, Millen certainly, and his shot snaps as his rifle swings up, as he drops. Bullets snick from everywhere, their sound booming back and forth along the canyon. He has only fired once and is down, completely aware, on the wrong side of his fire and he shoots carefully again to draw their shots and they come, four harmlessly high and nicely spaced out: there are two – Millen and another – below him in the canyon and two a bit higher on the right ridge, one of them that slipped. Nothing up the canyon or above on the cliff. With that knowledge he gathered himself and leaped over the fire against the cliff and one on the ridge made a good shot that cut his jacket and he could fall as if gut-shot in the hollow of deadfall. Until the fire died, he was almost comfortable.

In the growing dusk he watches the big Swede, who drove dogs very well, crawl toward Millen stretched out, face down. He watches him tie Millen's legs together with the laces of his mukluks and drag him backwards, plowing a long furrow and leaving the rifle sunk in the snow. He wastes no shot at their steady firing, and when they stop there are Millen's words still

You're surrounded. King isn't dead. Will you give

waiting, frozen in the canyon. He lay absolutely motionless behind the deadfall against the cliff, as if he were dead, knowing they would have to move finally. He flexed his feet continuously, and his fingers as he shifted the rifle no more quickly than a clock hand, moving into the position it would have to be when they charged him. They almost outwait him; it is really a question between the coming darkness and his freezing despite his invisible motions, but before darkness Millen had to move. Two of them were coming and he shifted his rifle slightly on the log to cover the left one – it must have been the long cold that made him mistake that for Millen – who dived out of sight, his shot thundering along the canyon, but Millen did not drop behind anything. Simply down on one knee, firing. Once, twice bullets tore the log and then he had his head up with those eyes staring straight down his sights and he fired two shots so fast the roar in the canyon sounded as one and Millen stood up, the whole length over him, whirled in that silent unmistakable way and crashed face down in the snow. He hears them dragging and chopping trees for a stage cache to keep the body, and in the darkness he chops handholds up the face of the cliff, step by step as he hoists himself and his pack out of another good shelter. As he has had to leave others.

3. *The Rat River, NWT:* Saturday, January 10, 1932
  Thursday, December 31, 1931
  Tuesday, July 28

In his regular round of each loophole he peers down the promontory toward their fires glaring up from behind the riverbank. They surround him on three sides, nine of them with no more than forty dogs, which in this cold means they already need more supplies than they can have brought with them. They will be making plans for something, suddenly, beyond bullets against his logs and guns and it will have to come soon. In the long darkness, and he can wait far easier than they. Dynamite. If they have any more to thaw out very carefully after blowing open the roof and stovepipe as darkness settled, a hole hardly big enough for one of them – a Norwegian, they were everywhere with their long noses – to fill it an instant, staring down at him gathering himself from the corner out of roof-sod and pipes and snow: the cabin barely stuck above the drifts but that one was gigantic to lean in like that, staring until he lifted his rifle and the long face vanished before his bullet passed through that space. But the hole was large enough for the cold to slide down along the wall and work itself into his trench, which would be all that saved him when they used the last of their dynamite. He began to feel what they had stalked him with all day: cold tightening steadily as steel around toes, face, around fingers.

In the clearing still nothing stirs. There is only the penumbra of light along the circle of the bank as if they had laid a trench-fire to thaw the entire promontory and were soundlessly burrowing in under him. Against the earth, his face momentarily knows them coming, there. Their flares were long dead, the sky across the river flickering with orange lights to vanish down into spruce and willows again, like the shadow blotting a notch in the eastern bank and he thrust his rifle through the chink and had almost got a shot away when a projectile arced against the sky and he jerked the gun out, diving, into the trench deep under the wall among the moose hides that could not protect him from the roof and walls tearing apart so loud it seemed most of himself had been blasted to the farthest granules of sweet, silent, earth. The sods and foot-thick logs he had built together where the river curled were gone and he would climb out and walk away as he always had, but first he pulled himself up and out between the splinters, still holding the rifle, just in time to see yellow light humpling through the snow toward him and he fired three times so fast it sounded in his ears as though his cabin was continuing to explode. The shadows around the light dance in one spot an instant but come on in a straight black line, lengthening down, faster, and the light cuts straight across his eyes and he gets away the fourth shot and the light tears itself into bits. He might have been lying on his back staring up into night and had the stars explode into existence above him. And whatever darkness is left before him then blunders away, desperately plowing away from him through the snow like the first one who came twice with a voice repeating at his door

I am Constable Alfred King, are you in there?

fist thudding the door the second time with a paper creaking louder than his voice so thin in the cold silence

I have a search warrant now, we have had complaints and if you don't open

and then plowing away in a long desperate scrabble through the sun-shot snow while the three others at the riverbank thumped their bullets hopelessly high into the logs but shattering the window again and again until they dragged King and each other headfirst over the edge while he placed lead carefully over them, snapping willow bits on top of them and still seeing, strangely, the tiny hole that had materialized up into his door when he flexed the trigger, still hearing the grunt that had wormed in through the slivers of the board he had whipsawn himself. Legs and feet wrapped in moose hide lay a moment across his window, level in the snow, jerking as if barely attached to a body knocked over helpless, a face somewhere twisted in gradually developing pain that had first leaned against his door, fist banging while that other one held the dogs at the edge of the clearing, waiting

Hallo? Hallo? This is Constable Alfred King of the Royal Canadian Mounted Police. I want to talk to you. Constable Millen has

and they looked into each other's eyes, once, through his tiny window. The eyes peering down into his – could he be seen from out of the blinding sun? – squinted blue from a boy's round face with a bulging nose bridged over pale with cold. King, of the Royal Mounted. Like a silly book title, or the funny papers. He didn't look it as much as Spike Millen, main snooper and tracker at Arctic Red River who baked pies and danced, everybody said, better than any man in the north. Let them dance hipped in snow, get themselves dragged away under spruce and dangling traps, asking, laying words on him, naming things

> You come across from the Yukon? You got a trapper's licence? The Loucheaux trap the Rat, up towards the Richardson Mountains. You'll need a licence, why not

Words. Dropping out of nothing into advice. Maybe he wanted a kicker to move that new canoe against the Rat River? Loaded down as it is. The Rat drops fast, you have to hand-line the portage anyway to get past Destruction City where those would-be Klondikers wintered in '98. He looked up at the trader above him on the wedge of gravel. He had expected at least silence. From a trader standing with the bulge of seven hundred dollars in his pocket; in the south a man could feed himself with that for two years. Mouths always full of words, pushing, every mouth falling open and dropping words from nothing into meaning. The trader's eyes shifted finally, perhaps to the junction of the rivers behind them, south and west, the united river clicking under the canoe. As he raised his paddle. The new rifle oiled and ready with its butt almost touching his knees as he kneels, ready to pull the canoe around.

4.   *Above Fort McPherson, NWT:* Tuesday, July 7, 1931

The Porcupine River, as he thought it was then, chuckled between the three logs of his raft. He could hear that below him, under the mosquitos probing the mesh about his head, and see the gold lengthen up the river like the canoe that would come toward him from the north where the sun just refused to open the spiky horizon. Gilded, hammered out slowly, soundlessly toward him the thick gold. He sat almost without breathing, watching it come like silence. And then imperceptibly the black spired riverbend grew pointed, stretched itself in a thin straight line double-bumped, gradually spreading a straight wedge below the sun through the golden river. When he had gathered that slowly into anger it was already too late to choke his fire; the vee had abruptly bent toward him, the bow man already raised this paddle; hailed. Almost it seemed as if a name had been blundered into the silence, but he did not move in his fury. The river chuckled again.

"...o-o-o-o..." the point of the wedge almost under him now. And the sound of a name, that was so clear he could almost distinguish it. Perhaps he already knew what it was, had long since lived this in that endlessly enraged chamber of himself, even to the strange Indian accent mounded below him in the canoe bow where the black hump of the stern partner moved them straight toward him out of the fanned ripples, crumbling gold. To the humps of his raft below on the gravel waiting to anchor them.

"What d'ya want."

"You Albert Johnson?"

It could have been the sternman who named him. The sun like hatchet-strokes across slanted eyes, the gaunt noses below him there holding the canoe against the current, their paddles hooked in the logs of his raft. Two Loucheaux half-faces, black and red kneeling in the roiled gold of the river, the words thudding softly in his ears.

You Albert Johnson?

One midnight above the Arctic Circle to hear again the inevitability of name. He has not heard it in four years, it could be to the very day since that Vancouver garden, staring into the evening sun and hear this quiet sound from these motionless – perhaps they are men kneeling there, perhaps waiting for him to accept again what has now been laid inevitably upon him, the name come to meet him in his journey north, come out of north around the bend and against the current of the Peel River, as they name that too, to confront him on a river he thought another and aloud where he would have found after all his years, at long last, only nameless silence.

You Albert Johnson?

"Yes," he said finally.

And out of his rage he begins to gather words together. Slowly, every word he can locate, as heavily as he would gather stones on a Saskatchewan field, to hold them for one violent moment against himself between his two hands before he heaves them up and hurls them – but they are gone. The ripples of their passing may have been smoothing out as he stares at where they should have been had they been there. Only the briefly golden river lies before him, whatever its name may be since it must have one, bending back somewhere beyond that land, curling back upon itself in its giant, relentless spirals down to the implacable, and ice-choked, arctic sea.

R. J. Brunt is a free-lance writer who worked for many years in the Arctic as a civil servant in the Department of National Defense and the Department of Transport. For two of these years he lived on Ellesmere Island at Alert. Established in 1950 primarily as a weather station to provide information for Canadian and American aircraft, Alert is the most northern permanent habitation in the world. Located at 82° 29′ north and 62° 15′ west, this small post has six months of darkness and six months of daylight but only about twenty-eight days in the whole year when the temperature rises above freezing. A number of Brunt's short stories that make use of this unusual setting have appeared in *North*.

During the fifties the establishment of geophysical and radar stations brought more white men into the Canadian Arctic than had been seen there since the search for the lost Franklin expedition. The camaraderie that developed among the men at isolated posts and the schemes that they devised to break the monotony are well illustrated in Brunt's story.

170

The Voice of the North
R. J. Brunt

There were some horrible shrieks and squawks coming out of the radio room and finally, I guess, the Chief couldn't stand it any longer.

"Can't you find some music?" he shouted.

"Sorry Chief," the radio operator called, "maybe it's the Northern Lights, but I can't get a thing."

If there was anything we lacked at our Arctic weather station it was good music. Of course we had a record-player and a collection of records but it wasn't quite the same and night after night, sometimes for weeks at a time, the radio bands went flat and our good music stations in London, Hamburg and Salt Lake City gave us nothing but a mush of static or distorted voices. But then when it did clear up there would be hour after hour of the world's finest music in English, German, Russian and heaven only knows what other languages all sucked into the Canadian Arctic by some mysterious property of the earth's magnetism, I suppose.

"Whew, how do you like this?" the radio operator called, and turned the gain of his receiver up high.

"This" was the raucous, querulous voice of a woman, calling and scolding in some foreign language.

"Gosh, how'd you like to be married to that?" The Chief winced as the nagging, imperious voice sawed on and on.

"Hey, turn it off, will you," he called and the operator obediently changed his wave length.

"What a voice," the cook said, shaking his head.

"Well anyway," the Chief said, "we don't have to listen to her." And he got up and began to fiddle with the record-player.

"I don't know why it is that women's voices usually sound so terrible over the air," he complained. "Although some of the European announcers are pretty nice," he amended.

"Not like that girl down in the States, eh?" grinned the radio operator who had come out of his office rubbing his ears.

"Now that was really something," the cook said admiringly.

"She say 'ah' just once," grinned Willi Auger, "and she melt the ice alla way to the Pole."

We all chuckled at that bit of wit from our gnome-like diesel mechanic and then fell silent as each of us recalled the sultry, sexy voice that had once caused so much havoc in the High Arctic.

"Wonder what ever happened to her?" the chief sighed wistfully.

"Probably old age," the met. officer snorted, for he was very old and cynical and doubtless had his own reasons, never mentioned, for his eight consecutive tours in the High Arctic.

I thought it prudent to remain silent. I knew her, you see.

She had been taken on by a small Detroit radio station as a disc jockey on their all-night show from midnight to eight, and although she didn't cause much of a stir among the jaded listeners down South, up here she was dynamite. For by some freak of radio propagation that tiny station, by no means as powerful as others in the very same area, came booming in (often for hours at a time) even to the remotest weather stations in the High Arctic chain.

It wasn't that she did anything or said anything different from what any other disc jockey said or did; it wasn't that she played any better or any worse records. But somehow she was the one woman in a million, even the one in ten million, whose radio speaking voice caused men – us men – to sit close to our receivers: panting, slavering.

"It's awfully lonely here, friends," she would sigh into her microphone, "won't you call me? I'd be glad to play your requests."

And hour after hour we'd listen indignantly as not one person, not a single soul, would answer her lovely voice.

"Why don't we call her up on the ham radio?" someone finally suggested.

"I don't think we can get a phone patch this time of night," the radio operator doubted, doing some fast calculations on time differences on the margin of his magazine.

"Well, try it!" we demanded.

And so he tuned up his ham rig and commenced to call and almost right away a loud voice came on his set, answering.

"Vee ee eight," came the voice, gratifyingly loud in our speaker, "this is double-you eight near Detroit, Michigan."

"Do you have a phone patch?" our operator demanded after the usual courtesies of ham radio were exchanged.

"Sure do! What can I do for you?"

Then we explained how we wanted to contact the studio of the small radio station in Detroit and talk to the girl disc jockey there.

"OK," the ham said, "I think we can do that. Just a moment while I connect us into the telephone lines and find the number."

And in a few moments we heard the familiar clicking and buzzing as he dialed and then to our delight we heard him talking to the girl – our girl!

"I've got some fellows up in the Canadian Arctic want to talk to you," he explained.

"You're kidding," we heard her gasp.

"Nope, I got a ham radio station here and they've got one up there too, and you can talk directly to them over your own telephone."

"How did they know about me?" she asked suspiciously.

"I dunno. Just a minute and I'll ask," he offered.

"Hey," he asked, "the young lady wants to know how you knew about her, you being away up there," he chuckled.

Swiftly we explained, interrupting each other and behaving (I know) like a bunch of adolescent kids, and soon our three-way conversation turned into a two-way exchange as we quite forgot about the American operator who silently manipulated his switches and controls to keep us in contact.

We talked for ten, twenty, even thirty minutes before the band started to go mushy and flat and for seconds at a time her voice, that lovely, lovely voice, became lost in the background noise until finally our control operator in Detroit broke in.

"I guess that's it for tonight, fellows. Your signals are fading too badly now. Give us a shout tomorrow, eh," he suggested.

And in the last few seconds of contact we agreed, if the band was in, to call him on the same frequency every night at midnight until we made contact again.

We had hardly signed off with the Detroit operator when another voice broke in. "Frobisher Bay calling," it said, "who were you guys talking to just then?"

Somewhat reluctantly we explained the situation to the ham operator on Baffin Island, far to the south of us, and told him of our sked with Detroit for the following night.

"We'd like to talk to her too," the Baffin Island operator suggested hopefully. "She sure has a lovely voice, eh?"

"Do you mean that you hear her there, too?"

"We sure do. We haven't heard a news broadcast all week," he laughed, "the boys here won't let me tune off her station!" And then with our promise to keep him posted we signed off for the night.

Well the word got around. Frobisher Bay told Pond Inlet and Pond Inlet told Cape Dyer and so, night after night, the owl shift workers in Detroit heard us all I guess, telling about our life in the far north as she patched us in to the station's facilities and everything (or most of everything!) we said was rebroadcast for the benefit of the American listeners.

As we competed for air time with all the other ham stations of the Arctic network (who broke in shamelessly on our phone patches) we would try to make our own adventures sound just a little more adventurous, our location just a little more remote and our lives just a little more lonely. Of course all the other stations of the net soon caught on and started to do the same (which may account for some of the stories you've heard of polar bears twelve feet high and of wolves that attack a taxiing aircraft!) and as time went on the tales got woolier and wilder until at some particularly wild flight of the imagination one of the other stations would

break in with a chortle or even an awed "Holy Cow!" and then, of course, they'd try to out-do us with equally fantastic tales of their own adventures.

It's incredible now to think that she actually believed those highly coloured yarns but that was what happened, and underneath her professional calm and insouciance there would come a note of worry as Cape Dyer would casually mention they were going to shoot a polar bear that was bothering their dogs.

"Oh, do be careful!" she'd breathe.

And the rest of us would chortle with delight as we nudged each other or heard some other station come on with a brief snort; for we knew perfectly well that no polar bear had been seen within a hundred miles of Cape Dyer in the past fifty years. But she didn't know; she worried about us.

Oh, it was fantastic. Her listeners (and I learned later that our contact made that tiny broadcast station as more and more people tuned in to her – and to us – and some even stayed up at night just to listen in) – they realized it was all phony and sheer romancing on our part. They knew, they accepted it and enjoyed it without probably believing a word we said. But she – she accepted it at face value, and believed every word.

Anyway, I went out that summer and such is the efficiency of modern air travel in the Arctic that exactly seventeen hours after leaving our station I was standing in the reception office of her station demanding her address or phone number. Reluctantly, suspiciously, the manager finally called her up.

"There's some fellow here to see you that's just down from the Arctic and wants your number. Do you want to see him?"

"Tell her it's Rick," I urged.

And then reluctantly the station manager passed the telephone to me.

"I'm just down on leave," I blurted. "Can I see you? Will you have supper with me?"

"But I've got to sleep," she laughed (oh that lovely voice). "I've got to work tonight," she protested.

"Tell 'em you're sick. Tell 'em anything. Take some holidays," I implored.

176   R. J. Brunt

"Are you married – or anything?" she asked then.

"Gosh no! Not yet," I added bravely.

She giggled delightfully. "Pick me up at six," she said and gave me the address.

I guess I was standing there like a love-sick bull or something when the manager coughed. "Have you never met Miss Rose?" he asked disbelievingly.

I shook my head; and then started. "Gosh, is that her name – Miss Rose?"

The manager slowly took off his glasses and stared at me. "Her name," he said carefully, "is Mildred Rose. She is unmarried. And," he added with a stern look, "she is a valued employee of this station."

I think I managed eventually to convince him that my intentions were entirely honourable (although I wasn't too sure of that myself) and he finally let me go with a pointed reminder that Miss Rose was due at work no later than eleven thirty. I promised faithfully to have her there: sober, intact and in fit state to work.

I don't think he believed me, though.

Somehow or other I managed to put in the hours until six o'clock when I presented myself at her boarding house only twenty minutes early.

"You will wait by the door while I call Miss Rose," the dragon who ran the place insisted. But it was worth the wait.

Oh Lord, but she was lovely. Tall and slender: everything that her voice had ever promised.

"Hi," I managed to stammer, "I'm Rick."

"I'm Mildred," she replied in that voice I knew so well.

"Oh, tell me," she said, "did your Chief get back from the bear hunt all right? I've been so worried!"

"Huh?" was all I could manage while I thought back frantically to try to figure out what she could be referring to.

"Oh yes, yes," I replied confidently. "Oh yes, he got back last week, hale and hearty." I had remembered just in time one of our fabrications involving a mythical and highly dangerous hunting trip over the sea ice – this in July when there was no ice.

"Oh I'm so glad," she sighed, "I worry so much about you boys up there."

I should have known! I should have realized right then that this girl, this kid – for she was scarcely out of her teens – had believed every one of our made-up, fantastic, incredible yarns of adventure in the High Arctic.

But our evening together was wonderful and so was the next day and the next, and days became weeks all too soon and then I had to start thinking of going back.

"Just two weeks left," I whispered one day as we lay on the beach together.

"Oh I hate to think of you going back there to face those terrible dangers," she said quickly.

I started to laugh.

I couldn't help it. Honestly, the most danger I've ever seen in eight years in the Arctic was when the door froze and I couldn't get in! There are risks up there, but not anything like the risks you run every day when you cross busy streets and ride in cars or buses. We know our risks and we know how to avoid them too. We've never had a serious accident at our station because we know it and the area around it like you know your own back yard. We respect the climate and the wildlife – what there is of it – but risks – hell! Our chief risk is that we might gain so much weight we couldn't get into the aircraft to go out!

And so I started to laugh.

"Oh Milly," I said, "it isn't like that at all."

"But the wolves?" she quavered.

"Oh heck, listen," I said, "those wolves are far more scared of us than we are of them. They would never attack a man who was on his feet."

She raised herself up on one elbow (oh lovely, lovely) and stared at me unbelievingly.

"And the polar bears?" she asked.

"Lord," I replied, "I've never even seen a polar bear! They don't come around settlements."

"And the musk-ox?" she asked, a note of rising hysteria in her voice, "you don't milk them?"

178   R. J. Brunt

I thought for a moment, trying to recall what had prompted this incredible question, before remembering that the boys at Floe Bay had cooked up a simply wonderful tale of a herd of musk-ox they kept "just for fresh milk" that came to an igloo-stable when summoned by a blast on a narwhal-tusk horn.

I roared with laughter.

"Oh, Milly! Of course not! It was just a story. You couldn't get within a hundred yards of a musk-ox, let alone milk one!"

"And the polar bear that was twelve feet high and the whale that towed your boat all the way from Cambridge Bay to Churchill – that was just a – a – tale too?"

"Why sure – gosh, we thought you'd like to hear some stories of the Arctic and nothing much ever happens there and so we made them up. Don't you see?"

Incredibly she started to cry. Then she pushed me away to kneel there, shaking and trembling, the tears running down her face and smearing her make-up, and I have never seen a woman look so desirable as she did at that moment.

"And my listeners," she sobbed, "you lied to them too?"

"Why, why – gosh Milly, they knew: why they must have known," I started to explain.

She slapped me then: just once. And then she got up and ran. I tried to follow but she scooped up her clothes and went into the bath house and later she refused to talk to me or even to let me get her a taxi home.

She didn't go on the air that night: or ever again.

That's why I didn't say anything when the Chief wondered what had become of "the girl with the wonderful voice."

After all, it was none of his affair.

Gabrielle Roy (1909-   ) was born in St. Boniface, Manitoba. After attending the normal school in Winnipeg, she taught for several years in rural Manitoba, before settling in Quebec. She began her literary career in 1937, writing stories and articles for *La Liberté* in St. Boniface and since that time she has won both the Governor General's Award for fiction and the Prix Femina (France). Taking as her theme the communion of the lonely individual with the world of nature, she has written such fine works as *La petite poule d'eau (Where Nests the Water Hen)* (1951); *La Montagne secrete (The Hidden Mountain)* (1962); *La Rivere sans repos (Windflower)* (1970); and *Children of My Heart* (1978).

Pierre Cadorai, the hero of *The Hidden Mountain,* is modelled on the trapper and painter, René Richard, whom Roy met when she was a journalist working for *Bullet des Agriculture.* On one occasion, when speaking about an exhibition of his work, she noted that the subjects he chose to paint were images of creation in its most denuded and most hostile forms – scrawny trees, sled dogs nearly dead from exhaustion, miserable cabins half-covered with snow, lonely silhouettes of men in heavy clothing struggling against the brutal wind.

These are the images that Pierre, too, paints as he makes his way from the Mackenzie Valley to Ungava, where he finds the "hidden mountain". The mountain is "incomparably proud", "incomparably alone". In looking at it, Pierre forgets "the hunger, the weariness, the barriers, the loneliness, the cruel anguish". So determined is he to capture the essence of the mountain in paint, that he ignores the warning of the Eskimo, Orok, to "beware of the mountain. It did not, perhaps, like to emerge from its mystery and from silence, it would perhaps be annoyed at his making its image, especially if he did not do a good job of it." This heedlessness almost costs Pierre his life.

The Hidden Mountain is not only about the artist's attempt to reproduce his vision of the truth. It is also about the artist's responsibility of sharing his vision with society:

> Pierre abruptly realized that he had done more than paint the glorious high mountain in a series of likenesses. At the same time, he had achieved something else, something vast, spacious in which he was like a bird winging through the air. How keenly, then, did he wish that some other eyes than his own would look at what he had done.

Gabrielle Roy's writing, like Pierre's painting, takes us beyond the North's physical attributes – its cold, its wild animals, its blizzards, and its desolate wastes – to its spirit.

The Hidden Mountain*
Gabrielle Roy

In the village on the coast the people lived in a handful of huts and cabins clustering around a weather-worn plank structure that was the store and residence of the company agent. Behind this was a singular man-made landscape: high pylons of steel, strange mechanisms hanging free in the air, some like huge kettledrums, others like giant saucers, a whole apparatus of strung wires, groaning chains, turning disks, by which the white men who lived in their prefabricated dwellings at the base of the pylons claimed that they could detect from afar, over the sea or under the sea, the coming of an invader.

That was the beginning of the mystery. For on these shores, who had ever seen the arrival of anyone who might be an invader? Surely the white men were curious people.

For example: to have installed right in the open, where blizzards were almost continuous, all these various objects, the very nature of which seemed to demand shelter, and which tirelessly hummed, clanked, clashed. Was this the right way to confront some future enemy who might emerge from the fog-filled ocean seas? Or from the equally enshadowed skies?

Thus at times Orok thought, who on other occasions rejoiced at the progress of events in the Eskimo land. For, to feed the machines and the men who tended them, small airplanes often enough made their appearance here, arriving with a great deal of noise and landing on the snow.

This was the fine side of the mystery, which had brought close the faraway cities, their inexhaustible supplies of goods, and their hospitals, too, for those who might fall grievously ill.

*Translated by Harry Binsse

Moreover, there was a bit of money to be earned from time to time in the service of the white men who served the machine.

Above all, the machines in themselves were passionately absorbing. Occasionally one of the whites had allowed Orok to watch their activity close to, and even to help in minor tasks of assembly or repair. Orok had learned that there was no necessity whatever to know the soul of the machine in order to make it stop or start again. And that was that, he thought, disposing of one of the mysteries taking place before his very eyes. The other, more disturbing perhaps, was the mystery of the Man-of-the-Magic-Pencil, who, in the weather-worn factor's residence, nursed by everyone, was little by little coming back to life.

Far more than at the things that floated and twisted in the wind, the village's curiosity had been aroused by this man whom, one day, it had seen coming from afar on the tundra, his feet swollen, half dead, and bearing against his breast, as though it had been a child, a few tattered drawings.

The old men, the most ancient of the village – the women, too – all often went to see this strange sight: a man, pale as the autumn snow, emaciated as a caribou's horns, who, seated on his bed with his back against the wall, throughout the almost constant night and by the glow of a single candle, made pictures of the sun.

Or yet again animals – the familiar animals of the muskeg: the thin-antlered caribou, the chubby bear, and others not known in these parts, for example, the great moose of the western country. And all seemed to open wide their eyes and their mouths as though in a terrible effort to speak. This, Orok by himself might perhaps not have discovered. Pierre had told him about it. He had said that he proposed to give the power of speech to beasts as well as to men – to all those who knew life's suffering.

So much for the mysteries that reigned throughout the long winter night of this tiny village in the Arctic wind. For, the Man-of-the-Magic-Pencil, who seemed to be toiling to elucidate the mystery of life, more and more laid them bare for others to see.

Indeed he was recovering. His gangrenous foot, although still frightfully swollen, was healing. And he labored. Once again reduced to the crayons of his childhood, he was refashioning the far-off landscapes of his life.

The Eskimos, and especially the whites, had wanted to ship him off by plane to Knob Lake and from there to Montreal or Quebec to get adequate care. He had refused. And stubbornly. When his arms were overflowing with pictures for them, then he would return to men. Not before. Doggedly, without the least complaint, day after day he was retracing in delicate small sketches the pathway of his life. Dwarfed forests of slender trees grew before the eyes of these people, who had never seen such things, and who were entranced. Such, then, was the great Mackenzie, such the swamplands of Manitoba! It is always joyful and good to see new things take substance before your eyes!

Pierre also drew the Eskimo faces hovering close around him, with their tight-lidded eyes that shone with the haunting desire common to every creature: to know what is – what can be – beyond the horizon.

Likewise he gave Orok a few drawing lessons. On paper and with a pencil Orok, to his own amazement, succeeded in depicting a tree that was a tree. A tree; what an amazing thing! And yet, Pierre would tell him, there are many people who, having them constantly before their eyes, no longer even see them. He said many things that stuck in the mind like a hunter's harpoon.

And in spite of everything this life was sweet to Pierre after all the endless camps where a man has no other living thing to look at, close at hand, than his fire.

One evening he heard on the snow, and not far off, a sound familiar beyond all others in his past, and one that plunged him wholly into it. A sled was arriving; you could hear the hearty voice urging on the dogs, the animals' eager, intermingled response when they know they are about to reach the place they will spend the night. Pierre thought himself back in the Mackenzie country. Steve was returning from his rounds. Pierre listened for the sounds, the door about to be thrust open. At last his companion was returning. That sturdy brother of his own – perhaps too frail – soul. Then he emerged from his dream.

"What's that?"

"It's the missionary Father who's just arrived," said Orok.

For here was yet another mystery! He, Orok, had attended the Protestant mission school. He had been told: God is in the great Holy Book. Then one day the missionary Father had passed through these parts. He said: Our God is living; He dwells in this little bit of bread.

"Whom should you believe? Who is right?" asked Orok.

"I don't know. Perhaps neither. Perhaps both."

"Perhaps you more than any," Orok said.

Not long after, having heard that a sick man was there, the missionary Father strode briskly in.

He was a man of towering size with a thick black beard, heavy, bushy eyebrows, his face almost wholly hidden except for the eyes, which possessed a surprising sweetness that could of a sudden captivate one's soul.

In earlier days Pierre had thought that he felt only scorn for these men of religion, be they Methodist, Anglican, or Catholic, who would venture even into these pitiless wastes, to upset, importune, and, on occasion, quarrel over simple peoples – all in the name of their God. Now he was no longer sure. In their attempt to explain it at any cost, it had seemed to him, these poor men succeeded only in making more obscure the mystery of suffering. But truly he was no longer sure.

The Father introduced himself: "André Le Bonniec; a Breton, of course, and from Ploërmel." Then he sat on the foot of the bed and offered his tobacco pouch.

"I don't smoke," said Pierre and, after a moment, for fear of hurting the other's feelings, felt obliged to explain: "I did have a liking for it and had almost acquired the habit. But tobacco is just one more weight to carry; then, too, it is hard to come by in the lonely places where I had to go. Was I, of my own free will, to chance straying from my chosen path just because I might need some tobacco? There are already so many things that whittle away freedom. I preferred making short shift of so tyrannical a need."

"Wisdom indeed," approved the priest. "I myself never had the courage." He admitted ingenuously, "My old pipe is such a consolation to me!"

He lit it, drew a few puffs, seemed at ease and humbly happy, encircled by the smoke as though encircled by heart-warming memories. Then, quite casually, his glance lit upon a living spot of color, slipped past it, then darted back as though suddenly aware of something crying for attention. Getting to his feet, the elderly missionary moved over to look more closely at the little painting on the wall. It was one of the studies of the mountain, done the summer before, which Pierre had succeeded in digging out of the snow and which, by some miracle, had not been too greatly damaged.

The priest, here in this dismal little room, stared at it. He sighed. An intense emotion gripped his heart. He was almost an old man; though not yet sixty, he seemed closer to three score and ten. And it was because, out of the sixty years of his existence, he had given thirty to the missions of the great North. Thirty years of ceaseless journeying, on dog sleds or snow-shoes, though occasionally, particularly in recent years, by airplane. For all that, though, the little isolated posts remained just as far off, where he went to say and say again, to men clad in the skins of animals, dwelling in huts or igloos – to say and to repeat that God is light, life, and love. Thirty years of such an inhuman life had slipped by, and never had he uttered a word of complaint, either for himself or for the frightful misery he had everywhere seen about him. But now, at the sight of a tiny painting of summer, his heart burst with sweetness; he was aware of his distraught longing for warmth, for tenderness; tears were flooding his eyes.

"Rebels!" he murmured. "How does it happen that every lovely thing done in this world should be an act of protest? To create," he muttered to himself, as though he had only just discovered it, "is this not to protest with all one's soul? Unless...unless," he added, deep in thought, "it be indeed a secret collaboration...."

He could not tear himself away from the sketch. And yet it was a very simple little thing. Here is what might be discerned upon it: in the centre, a part of the face of a stone mountain, in a brilliant emerald green, bewitch-ing and strange. This green ran down to mingle with the white caribou moss on the shore of a lake of limpid water, which yet retained its brilliance for being a little in shadow. What invested the whole with meaning, however, remained as though invisible – or at least barely perceptible. Beyond the green rock there opened what might be called a perspective, a minute slit showing distant depth, even though the whole painting was not twice the size of a man's hand. You looked at this narrow opening – a crevice no thicker than a thread – on a distance invisible, luminous; and you held your breath, you were captured by quiet expectation; you could say to yourself, yes, this world is lovely and compassionate; this world is lustrous.

At last the Father regained his composure. He returned to the bed and sat down, began avidly examining the other sketches – a dozen or so – which Pierre explained he had been able to rescue from beneath the snow in his camp when it had been raided by a bear. Explained how, while journeying, he could not obtain canvas and therefore used for painting his pictures small panels of wood, whittled by himself as thin as he could make them; out of sheer economy he had almost always used both sides of these panels.

When he saw this – the one face and the other of these tiny surfaces covered with vivid landscapes – the priest was again beset with emotion.

"Forgive me." he said, "I'm an old sentimentalist, a little overinclined to tears. It's because I've not seen such things for a long time. Loveliness – forgive me – takes me by surprise. And, after all, it is always endlessly surprising. What is it, really? We say the beautiful, beauty, but what is it? What purpose does it serve? We don't know, if we come right down to it – any more than you do, I suppose. And here you've attained it by the saddest and the most meager of means."

Now he was examining, one by one, the delicate sketches, each turned out within a few minutes, that covered Pierre in his bed as leaves cover the earth at the foot of a tree.

"Yes, I've seen that," he was saying, as he looked at a group of dogs crushed with weariness on the evening after a long day; near them shone the campfire; the men were preparing food. "And this too," he exclaimed eagerly, at the sight of a cabin in the heart of an infinite forest of tiny trees, every last one of them bent with distress. "This also," the first tiny clouds of spring, pink, downy, like newborn birds swimming in freedom over the heavy life of men. "I have seen all that," he was about to cry, and then

remained silent, seized by immense respect. For had he truly seen these things before this man of light came to show them to him?

At a glance, likewise, he realized the utter paucity of means in which these drawings had come to birth: the smoky candle, the miserable scraps of paper, the stuffy room, the loneliness; his soul swelled with indignation. Was that the way to treat this child, among all others beloved of men, he who opens their eyes, he who also suddenly opens wide between them the great doorways of communication? Surely nothing could possibly be too fine, too rich for such creatures. Meanwhile an idea was taking shape in his mind, so greatly fertile in invention. He had got to his feet, unable in his excitement to stay still, striding up and down the tiny rooms. These great wanderers, after all, are quite incapable of holding long in check their eternal need to keep moving. And here was what he said as he paced to and fro:

"Listen, my boy, in Montreal I have a few friends. Even a little influence. Yes, it may seem strange, but that's the way it is. Far from everyone, I still have friends. Would you trust me with your studies, a few of your sketches? I'll make it my business to send them to those friends. We shall see what they think of them. We'll have their opinion. Not that it is something we can't do without, but – all things considered – it might be useful. Anyway, I think their opinion will be the same as mine. After that, I'll urge them to organize a little exhibition in Montreal.... Now come, let me finish what I'm saying," he interrupted himself, having glimpsed a gesture of protest. "For, after all, why do you think you're wearing yourself out with painting? For yourself? For me? No, no! Surely you're laboring for people you never saw, the great general mass. That's the way it is – strange enough in its essence, but true. The greatest among us work for unknown men and women, who all too often, sadly enough, will understand no part of it."

His eyes glittering, he strode the length of the room, exultant in spirit, then turned on his heel to take the few strides back.

"What a mysterious, extraordinary attraction is that of the unknown upon the soul of an artist! Somehow I think I understand it; yes, I guess at it; it must be one of the strongest attractions there can be...next only to God's upon our poor souls...."

He had lost the thread of his thought and showed himself a little vexed in consequence; then, finding it again, his eyes resumed their full sheen of tenderness.

"Well, then; your studies are exhibited down there, in the most favorable setting. I can see the result. Our pictures begin to sell...one, two... then ten, twenty.... Yes, they sell, I tell you; people down there, in their insipid and shut-in cities must have forgotten the great cries of the heart. And sell they must," he added gently, at the sight of Pierre's stricken countenance. "They must, if you are to follow your driving urge, to attain summits which neither you nor I can foresee and – above all else – to communicate with your neighbor, my son; for do you not love him?"

Then, carried away with his inspiration, he exclaimed, "Don't you see, you hard-headed child? There is the heart of him who gives and the heart of him who receives; occasionally it happens that the one and the other lie within the same breast; what comes from the one fills the other heart with joy; and then alone does it happen, perhaps, that what flows forth is that which we call beauty. I do not know, but think about it; it is possible that I speak truth."

Pierre was shaking his head, taking on a sullen look, saying that all this was not for him, at least not yet; he was not ready, would not be ready for a long while, it seemed to him, for this ordeal of confrontation that appalled him.

Nonetheless, there soon began to be fulfilled a portion of these things.

In less time than one would have thought possible, Father Le Bonniec had had shipped from Montreal a whole collection of paints. Joyfully he brought them to Pierre.

"What is this misplaced pride?" he exploded, in response to the latter's protests. All this had cost him very nearly nothing. Not much more than the shipping expense. Friends were kind; they were there to help, after all. What was more, if Pierre was so eager not to put himself in debt to as good a comrade as the Father thought himself to be, well, then let him give in return no matter which of the small sketches. And he would, said he, think that he himself was getting the better of the bargain.

But Pierre, at the sight of the colors, was already forgetting everything else. In variety and number they were more complete than anything he had ever possessed.

"Look here, my son," the priest was saying. "Lovely vermilion; use it generously, for it is the ardent color. Paint the way you are – quick impulsive, nervous. I have no patience with those small-spirited daubers of today who work in leaden tones. Modern grisaille, they call it. They quench, it seems to me, that which one should make shine. Of course I am old, outmoded; perhaps I don't understand. All the same, the great painters spread color gaily. Brueghel, for instance, that old scoundrel. I remember "The Wedding Dance". It fairly exudes color everywhere. And Delacroix! As for Gauguin! Were those fellows afraid of laying it on? Lay it on thick, my dear boy, and you will realize, later on, when you go to Paris, to Amsterdam, to London, to see the works of the masters, how wild, often, is genius...."

When spring returned and Pierre was practically well again, he took Orok to help him with the hunting and carrying, and journeyed by easy stages back to his mountain. All winter he had never stopped meditating upon it. There, on the spot, he made some three dozen sketches and thought he would use them later for more ambitious paintings. The Father was delighted with them. Yet Pierre, with only this bare handful of studies, felt himself a pauper. This confrontation facing him – mysterious as it was – the confrontation of the work and the world was to him a constant source of terror.

One morning he took his seat in a small twin-engined navy plane. The aircraft left the ground. Down below, tiny human forms moved about, already reduced to the size of insects, their movements pathetic in so vast and lonely a setting. Oh, dear Orok! Dear primitive life! Would there ever be anything in the world so tenderly fraternal!

The plane was speeding toward the south.

Without effort, without pain, without misery, Pierre flew over a vastness similar to so many vastnesses he had traversed on foot; could such a thing even be possible! From the top of the sky, cradled like a bird in the blue, he saw himself toiling below, just as he would have seemed, in another day, from the top of the same sky: a human ant struggling along with everything he owned upon his back. What purpose, then, did the presence of such an ant serve upon the earth?

The muskeg of Ungava, the savannas of the Manitoban North, the endless forests of the Upper and Lower Mackenzie – all this, which he had spent years in crossing, and at the cost of the most exhausting effort, suddenly shrank in his eyes, diminished, became no more than just a few images, a few fleeting images, and all the rest – toil, infinite pain – was swept away. Still, it is true – he had a little too much forgotten it lately – that life in its essence is brief. How much of it really remained to him? Yet, his fated task – had he done more than merely broach it?

Dread grasped his being as though, in his depths, when facing the work still to be accomplished, he had never been more than a timid child, a newborn soul, too fragile for its own bold vision.

This Canadian wasteland, this boundless Siberia of our country – how could it indeed compare with that other solitude toward which he was winging, the utterly mysterious solitude of streets filled with people, with footsteps, and with light!

Associate editor / Heather Pringle
Design / David Shaw & Associates Ltd.
Composition / Accurate Typesetting Ltd.
Colour separation / Artcraft Engravers Ltd.
Colour printing / Curtis Company Ltd.
Manufacture / John Deyell Company